GCSE OCR Gateway
Chemistry
Higher Workbook

This book is for anyone doing **GCSE OCR Gateway Chemistry** at higher level.

It's full of **tricky questions**... each one designed to make you **sweat** — because that's the only way you'll get any **better**.

There are questions to see **what facts** you know. There are questions to see how well you can **apply those facts**. And there are questions to see what you know about **how science works**.

It's also got some daft bits in to try and make the whole experience at least vaguely entertaining for you.

What CGP is all about

Our sole aim here at CGP is to produce the highest quality books — carefully written, immaculately presented and dangerously close to being funny.

Then we work our socks off to get them out to you — at the cheapest possible prices.

Contents

Module C1 — Carbon Chemistry

Atoms, Molecules and Compounds 1
Chemical Equations 2
Emulsifiers 4
Cooking and Chemical Change 5
Perfumes 6
Kinetic Theory and Forces Between Particles 7
Solutions 9
Paints and Pigments 10
Special Pigments 11
Polymers 12
Polymers and Their Uses 13
Hydrocarbons — Alkanes 14
Hydrocarbons — Alkenes 15
Fractional Distillation of Crude Oil 16
Hydrocarbon Properties — Bonds 18
Cracking 19
Use of Fossil Fuels 21
Burning Fuels 22
The Evolution of the Atmosphere 23
The Carbon Cycle 25
Air Pollution and Acid Rain 26
Mixed Questions — Module C1 27

Module C2 — Chemical Resources

The Earth's Structure 30
Plate Tectonics 32
Volcanic Eruptions 33
The Three Different Types of Rock 34
Construction Materials 36
Extracting Pure Copper 37
Alloys 38
Building Cars 40
Acids and Bases 41
Reactions of Acids 42
Fertilisers 44
Preparing Fertilisers 46
The Haber Process 47
Minimising the Cost of Production 48
Salt 49
Mixed Questions — Module C2 50

Module C3 — Chemical Economics

Energy Transfer in Reactions 53
Measuring the Energy Content of Fuels 54
Chemical Reaction Rates 55
Collision Theory 56
Rate of Reaction Data 58
Reacting Masses 60
Calculating Masses in Reactions 61
Atom Economy 62
Percentage Yield 63
Chemical Production 64
Allotropes of Carbon 66
Mixed Questions — Module C3 68

Module C4 — The Periodic Table

The History of the Atom ... 71
Atoms ... 72
Elements and Isotopes ... 73
History of the Periodic Table ... 74
Electron Shells ... 75
Ionic Bonding ... 77
Ions and Ionic Compounds ... 78
Covalent Bonding ... 79
Group 1 — Alkali Metals ... 80
Group 7 — Halogens ... 82
Metals ... 84
Superconductors and Transition Metals ... 86
Thermal Decomposition and Precipitation ... 87
Water Purity ... 89
Testing Water Purity ... 90
Mixed Questions — Module C4 ... 91

Module C5 — How Much?

The Mole ... 94
Reacting Masses and Empirical Formulas ... 95
Concentration ... 97
Titrations ... 100
Gas Volumes ... 103
Following Reactions ... 104
Equilibrium ... 106
Changing Equilibrium ... 107
The Contact Process ... 109
Strong and Weak Acids ... 110
Precipitation Reactions ... 113
Preparing Insoluble Salts ... 114
Mixed Question — Module C5 ... 115

Module C6 — Chemistry Out There

Redox Reactions ... 118
Rusting of Iron ... 120
Electrolysis ... 121
Fuel Cells ... 125
CFCs and the Ozone Layer ... 127
Hardness of Water ... 130
Alcohols ... 132
Fats and Oils ... 134
Using Plant Oils ... 136
Detergents ... 137
Mixed Questions — Module C6 ... 138

Published by CGP

Editors:
Katie Braid, Mary Falkner, Ben Fletcher, David Hickinson, Helen Ronan.

Contributors:
Michael Aicken, Mike Bossart, Mike Dagless, Ian H Davis, Max Fishel, Rebecca Harvey
Andy Rankin, Sidney Stringer Community School, Paul Warren, Chris Workman.

ISBN: 978 1 84762 622 6

With thanks to Philip Dobson, Chris Elliss, Paul Jordin, Jamie Sinclair and Hayley Thompson for the proofreading.

With thanks to Laura Stoney for the copyright research.

Groovy website: www.cgpbooks.co.uk

Printed by Elanders Ltd, Newcastle upon Tyne.
Jolly bits of clipart from CorelDRAW®
Based on the classic CGP style created by Richard Parsons.

Atoms, Molecules and Compounds

Q1 Say whether each of the following refers to the **nucleus** or the **electrons** within an atom.

a) Has a negative charge. .... **b)** Found at the centre of an atom. ....

c) Has a positive charge. .... **d)** Involved in chemical bonding. ....

Q2 **True** or **false**?

	True	False
a) In ionic bonding, ions lose or gain electrons to give atoms.	☐	☐
b) Ions with opposite charges attract each other.	☐	☐
c) Elements that lose electrons form positive ions.	☐	☐
d) Covalent bonding involves sharing electrons.	☐	☐

Q3 Complete the table showing the **names**, **displayed formulas**, **molecular formulas** and the number of **covalent bonds** for three carbon compounds.

NAME	DISPLAYED FORMULA	MOLECULAR FORMULA	NUMBER OF COVALENT BONDS
a)	H–C(H)(H)–H	b)	c)
ETHANE	H–C(H)(H)–C(H)(H)–H	d)	e)
PROPANE	H–C(H)(H)–C(H)(H)–C(H)(H)–H	f)	g)

Q4 The **displayed** formula for **ethanol** is shown on the right.

H–C(H)(H)–C(H)(H)–O–H

a) What is the molecular formula of ethanol? ....

b) How many atoms does a molecule of ethanol contain?

....

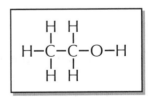

Q5 **Chemical formulas** are used to show elements and compounds.

a) What are the chemical formulas of the following elements and compounds?

i) oxygen gas .... **ii)** carbon dioxide .... **iii)** sulfuric acid ....

b) State how many oxygen atoms there are in the following compounds.

i) H_2O .... **ii)** Na_2CO_3 .... **iii)** CO ....

Chemical Equations

Q1 This **equation** shows the formation of **carbon dioxide** when carbon is burned in air:

$$C + O_2 \rightarrow CO_2$$

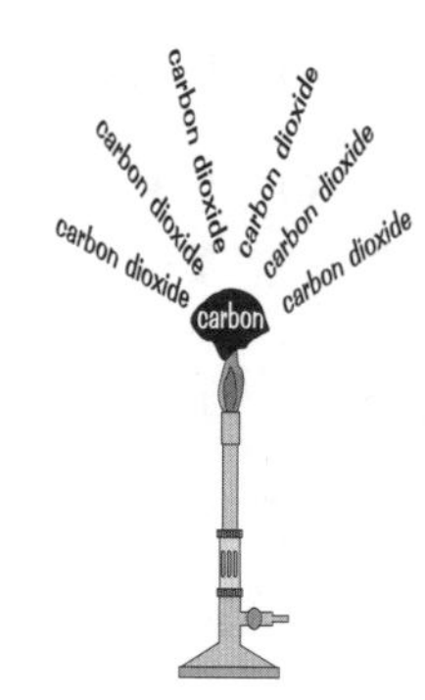

a) Name the **reactant(s)** in this equation.

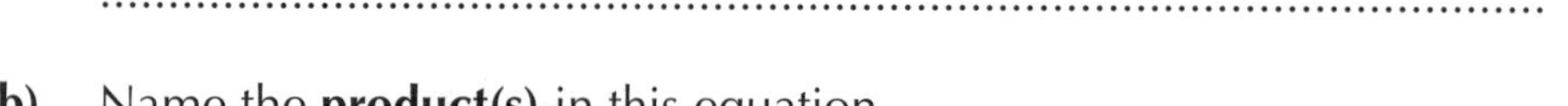

b) Name the **product(s)** in this equation.

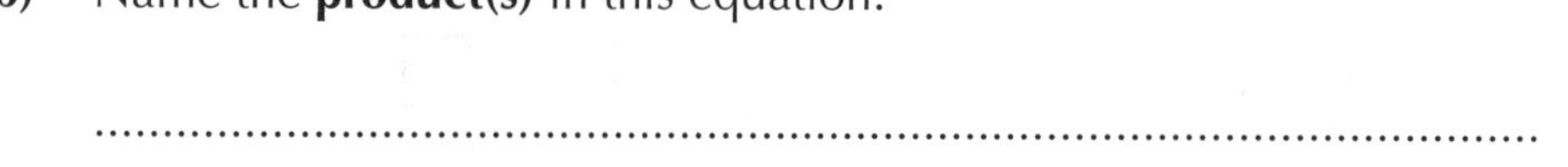

c) How can you tell the equation is **balanced**?

Q2 Here is the equation for the production of **carbon monoxide** from a poorly ventilated charcoal flame. It is **not** balanced correctly.

$$C + O_2 \rightarrow CO$$

Circle the **correctly balanced** version of this equation.

$C + O_2 \rightarrow CO_2$

$C + O_2 \rightarrow 2CO$

$2C + O_2 \rightarrow 2CO$

Q3 A book describes a reaction as follows: "**Methane** (CH_4) burns in **oxygen** (O_2) to form **carbon dioxide** (CO_2) and **water** (H_2O)."

a) What are the **reactants** and the **products** in this reaction?

Reactants: .... Products: ....

b) Write the **word equation** for this reaction.

....

c) Write the **balanced symbol equation** for the reaction.

....

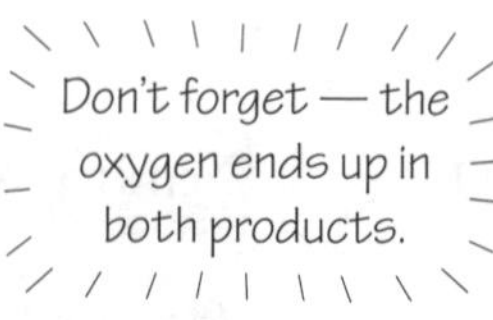

Don't forget — the oxygen ends up in both products.

Top Tips: The most important thing to remember with balancing equations is that you can't change the **little numbers** — if you do that then you'll change the substance into something completely different. Just take your time and work through everything logically.

Chemical Equations

Q4 **Lithium** reacts with **water** to produce **lithium hydroxide** (LiOH) and **hydrogen**.

a) Write the word equation for this reaction.

....

b) Write the balanced symbol equation for this reaction.

....

Q5 This unbalanced equation shows **magnesium chloride** being made from **magnesium carbonate**.

$$MgCO_3 + HCl \rightarrow MgCl_2 + H_2O + CO_2$$

a) Write the word equation for this reaction.

....

b) Write the balanced symbol equation for this reaction.

....

Q6 Add **one** number to each of these equations so that they are **correctly balanced**.

a) .... CuO + ... HBr → .... $CuBr_2$ + ... H_2O

b) .... H_2 + ... Br_2 → .... HBr

c) .... $NaOH$ + ... H_2SO_4 → .... Na_2SO_4 + ... H_2O

I've left spaces in front of all the molecules so I don't give the game away. If a molecule doesn't need a number in front, just leave it blank.

Q7 **Balance** these equations.

a) .... $NaOH$ + ... $AlBr_3$ → .... $NaBr$ + ... $Al(OH)_3$

b) .... Fe + ... O_2 → .... Fe_2O_3

c) .... $H{-}\underset{H}{\overset{H}{C}}{-}H$ + ... $Cl{-}Cl$ → .... $Cl{-}\underset{Cl}{\overset{Cl}{C}}{-}Cl$ + ... $H{-}H$

d) .... MgO + ... HNO_3 → .... $Mg(NO_3)_2$ + ... H_2O

e) .... $CuSO_4$ + ... $NaOH$ → .... $Cu(OH)_2$ + ... Na_2SO_4

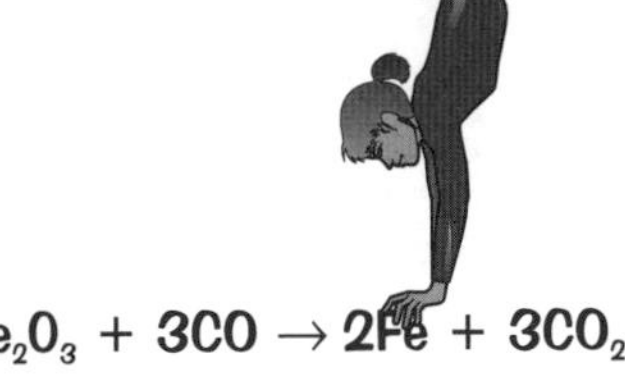

$Fe_2O_3 + 3CO \rightarrow 2Fe + 3CO_2$

Q8 Write the symbol equation for the reaction of **sodium carbonate** with **sulfuric acid**. The products of the reaction are **carbon dioxide**, **water** and **sodium sulfate** (Na_2SO_4).

....

Top Tip: Balancing equations is a simple matter of **trial and error** — keep changing one thing at a time until eventually you get the same number of each atom on both sides.

Emulsifiers

Q1 Imran is investigating the effects of different food additives on a mixture of **olive oil** and **water**. He sets up four flasks containing equal volumes of oil and water. He adds nothing else to the first one, and equal volumes of either **additive A**, **B** or **C** to the others. Then he gives them all a good shake and leaves them on a windowsill. After five days he notes their appearance in this table.

Additive used	Appearance after 5 days
None	Oil floating on water. Unpleasant smell.
A	Oil floating on water. No smell.
B	Oil floating on water. Unpleasant smell.
C	Oil and water mixed. Unpleasant smell.

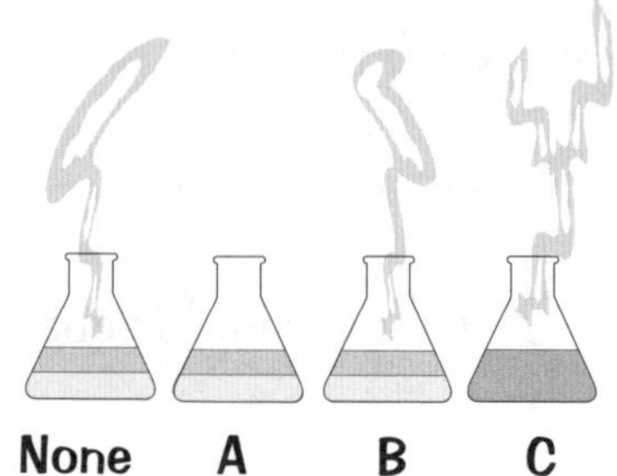

a) Antioxidants are additives that prevent foods 'going off' as quickly, by preventing them from reacting with oxygen. Which one of the additives is:

i) An antioxidant? ....

ii) An emulsifier? ....

b) Justify your answers to part **a)**.

i) ....

ii) ....

c) Why does Imran set up a flask with no additives added?

....

d) Name a food that often contains an emulsifier. ....

Q2 **Lecithin** is added to chocolate drinks in order to prevent the oils separating out from the water. The diagram shows a molecule of lecithin.

a) Label the **hydrophilic** part and the **hydrophobic** part of the lecithin molecule.

b) Briefly explain how this molecule stops the oil and water parts of chocolate drinks from separating into two different layers.

....

....

....

Cooking and Chemical Change

Q1 When meat or eggs are cooked the **protein** molecules they contain are **denatured**.

a) Explain how cooking causes this chemical change to proteins.

....

....

....

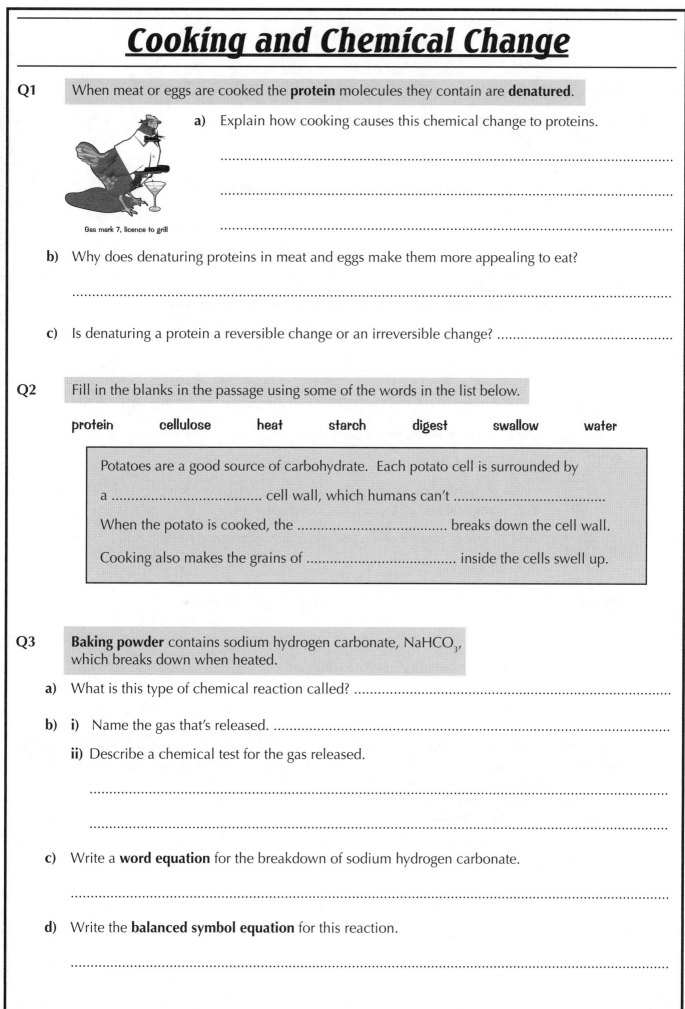

Gas mark 7, licence to grill

b) Why does denaturing proteins in meat and eggs make them more appealing to eat?

....

c) Is denaturing a protein a reversible change or an irreversible change? ....

Q2 Fill in the blanks in the passage using some of the words in the list below.

protein **cellulose** **heat** **starch** **digest** **swallow** **water**

Potatoes are a good source of carbohydrate. Each potato cell is surrounded by

a .... cell wall, which humans can't ....

When the potato is cooked, the .... breaks down the cell wall.

Cooking also makes the grains of .... inside the cells swell up.

Q3 **Baking powder** contains sodium hydrogen carbonate, $NaHCO_3$, which breaks down when heated.

a) What is this type of chemical reaction called? ....

b) **i)** Name the gas that's released. ....

ii) Describe a chemical test for the gas released.

....

....

c) Write a **word equation** for the breakdown of sodium hydrogen carbonate.

....

d) Write the **balanced symbol equation** for this reaction.

....

Perfumes

Q1 New perfumes are sometimes tested on **animals**.

a) Give one reason **for** testing cosmetic products on animals.

....

b) Explain why testing of cosmetic products on animals is **banned** in the EU.

....

....

Q2 A fruity smelling ester can be made by reacting **ethanol** with **ethanoic acid**.

a) Write a word equation for the **general** reaction used to make an ester.

....

b) Write numbers in the boxes to put the instructions into the right order for making this ester.

- ☐ Warm the flask gently on an electric heating plate for 10 minutes.
- ☐ Put 15 cm^3 of ethanoic acid into a 100 cm^3 conical flask.
- ☐ When the flask is cool enough to handle, pour its contents into a 250 cm^3 beaker containing 100 cm^3 of sodium carbonate solution.
- ☐ Add 15 cm^3 of ethanol and a few drops of concentrated sulfuric acid.
- ☐ Turn off the heat.

c) Suggest which of the above steps is carried out to speed up the reaction.

....

d) What is the purpose of the sodium carbonate solution?

....

Q3 A chemist was asked by an **aftershave company** to make some new scents. Her new compounds were then **tested** to see if they were suitable for use in aftershaves. The results of the tests are summarised in the table on the right.

Scent	Does it evaporate easily?	Does it dissolve in water?	Does it react with water?
A	yes	no	yes
B	yes	yes	no
C	yes	no	no
D	no	no	no

a) Which one of these would you use as the scent in an aftershave and why?

....

....

b) Suggest a further test that should be carried out before the chemical can be used in the aftershave.

....

Kinetic Theory and Forces Between Particles

Q1 For each description below, say whether it refers to the particles of a **solid**, a **liquid** or a **gas**.

a) There are virtually no forces between particles. ....

b) The particles can vibrate but cannot move from place to place. ....

c) The particles can move around but tend to stick together. ....

d) There are strong forces holding the particles together. ....

e) The particles move freely in straight lines. ....

f) There is no fixed volume or shape. ....

g) There is a fixed volume, but no fixed shape. ....

Q2 Choose from the words in the list to fill in the blanks in this paragraph.

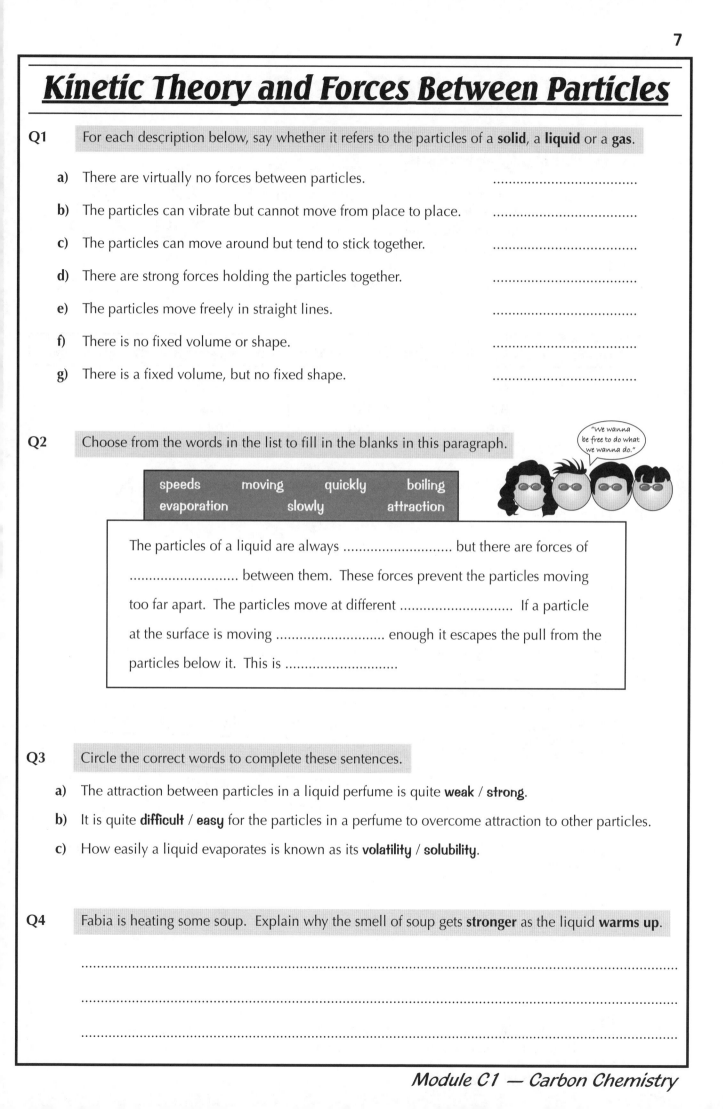

"We wanna be free to do what we wanna do."

speeds	moving	quickly	boiling
evaporation	slowly	attraction	

The particles of a liquid are always .... but there are forces of .... between them. These forces prevent the particles moving too far apart. The particles move at different .... If a particle at the surface is moving .... enough it escapes the pull from the particles below it. This is ....

Q3 Circle the correct words to complete these sentences.

a) The attraction between particles in a liquid perfume is quite **weak** / **strong**.

b) It is quite **difficult** / **easy** for the particles in a perfume to overcome attraction to other particles.

c) How easily a liquid evaporates is known as its **volatility** / **solubility**.

Q4 Fabia is heating some soup. Explain why the smell of soup gets **stronger** as the liquid **warms up**.

....

....

....

Kinetic Theory and Forces Between Particles

Q5 Lucy tested chemicals X, Y and Z to see how suitable they were for use in liquid **air fresheners**.

A volunteer sat at one end of a room and a bottle containing the chemical was opened at the other end. She asked the volunteer to raise a hand when he or she **smelt** the chemical. The time between the bottle being opened and the volunteer's hand being raised was recorded. The test was repeated with different volunteers and the results are shown in the table below.

Chemical	Time (volunteer 1) /s	Time (volunteer 2) /s	Time (volunteer 3) /s	Average time /s
X	45	32	36	
Y	112	98	103	
Z	278	246	243	

a) Complete the table by working out the **average time** for each of the three chemicals.

b) Explain why the volunteers didn't smell the chemicals as soon as the bottles were opened.

....

....

....

c) What does the data tell you about the **volatility** of the chemicals? Circle your answer.

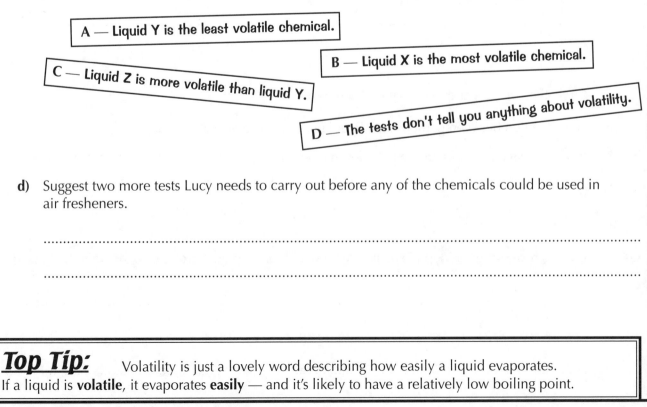

A — Liquid Y is the least volatile chemical.

B — Liquid X is the most volatile chemical.

C — Liquid Z is more volatile than liquid Y.

D — The tests don't tell you anything about volatility.

d) Suggest two more tests Lucy needs to carry out before any of the chemicals could be used in air fresheners.

....

....

Top Tip: Volatility is just a lovely word describing how easily a liquid evaporates. If a liquid is **volatile**, it evaporates **easily** — and it's likely to have a relatively low boiling point.

Solutions

Q1 Tick the correct boxes to show whether the following statements are **true** or **false**.

		True	False
a)	A solute is made by dissolving a solid in a liquid.	☐	☐
b)	A solvent is the liquid that the solid is dissolving into.	☐	☐
c)	A solution is a mixture of a solute and a solvent that doesn't separate out.	☐	☐
d)	A substance that will dissolve in a solvent is described as insoluble.	☐	☐
e)	Lots of esters make good solvents.	☐	☐

Q2 Read the following sentences and list all the **solutes**, **solvents** and **solutions** mentioned.

Salt dissolves in water to form brine. A tincture can be made by dissolving iodine in alcohol. Gold is soluble in mercury and this mixture is an amalgam.

a) Solutes ....

b) Solvents ....

c) Solutions ....

Q3 A chemical company is testing three new solvents for dry-cleaning.

a) What mass of solvent A is needed to dissolve 50 g of paint?

....

....

....

	Solvent		
	A	B	C
Cost per 100 g (£)	0.40	0.15	0.20
Solubility of paint (g per 100 g of solvent)	12.1	0.1	10.3

b) Which solvent would you choose to buy if you were a buyer for a dry-cleaning company? Explain your choice.

....

....

Q4 Circle the letters of any statements that correctly explain why **nail varnish** won't dissolve in **water**.

A Water is not a good solvent.

B The forces between the molecules of nail varnish are stronger than those between the molecules of water and the molecules of nail varnish.

C Water is only good for dissolving substances that are non-toxic.

D The forces between the molecules of water are stronger than those between the molecules of water and the molecules of nail varnish.

Paints and Pigments

Q1 Draw lines to match each term on the left with the correct description on the right.

pigment	holds pigment particles to a surface
colloid	makes the paint thinner and easy to spread
solvent	tiny particles dispersed in another material
binding medium	the substance that gives paint its colour

Q2 Which of the following statements are **true** and which are **false**?

		True	False
a)	A colloid is formed when solid particles dissolve into a liquid.	☐	☐
b)	Emulsion paints are colloids.	☐	☐
c)	Oil paints are colloids.	☐	☐
d)	The particles in colloids are always solids.	☐	☐
e)	The particles in colloids are so small that they stay dispersed and do not settle.	☐	☐

Q3 Circle the correct words to complete the sentences below.

a) Gloss paints are **oil-based** / **water-based**. Emulsion paints are **oil-based** / **water-based**.

b) Paint dries as the **solvent** / **binding medium** evaporates.

c) In oil-based paints the solvent is **oil** / **something that dissolves oil**.

Q4 Ann is painting the outside of her front door using an **oil-based gloss paint**. She brushes on a thin coat of paint and leaves it to dry for a whole day.

a) Give one property of oil paint that would make it a good choice for painting a front door.

....

b) Explain how an oil paint dries.

....

....

....

....

Special Pigments

Q1 **Thermochromic pigments** have many uses.

Suggest why themochromic pigments are suited to each of these uses:

a) Colouring a spoon that is used for feeding a **baby**.

....

....

b) Painting a design on a mug that is used for **hot drinks**.

....

....

Q2 Draw lines to join each statement to the **type of pigment** it relates to.

can become transparent when heated

used in thermometers

absorb and store energy and release it as light

used in road signs

PHOSPHORESCENT PIGMENTS

THERMOCHROMIC PIGMENTS

glow in the dark

can be mixed with acrylic paints to give a wide range of colour changes

used in emergency exit signs

Q3 The diagram shows two watches with **glow-in-the-dark hands**. One is from **1950**, the other is from **2006**.

1950 **2006**

a) Radioactive paint was used on the hands of the watch from 1950. What type of paint was probably used on the watch from **2006**?

....

b) Explain why the type of paint used was changed.

....

....

Polymers

Q1 Indicate whether the following sentences are **true** or **false**?

		True	False
a)	Making monomers from polymers is called polymerisation.	☐	☐
b)	Alkene molecules are often used as the monomers.	☐	☐
c)	Plastics are made up of lots of polymer chains.	☐	☐
d)	The atoms within the polymer chains are held together by covalent bonds.	☐	☐

Q2 **Addition polymers** are formed when **unsaturated monomers** link together.

a) What is an unsaturated compound?

....

b) Name two conditions needed to make addition polymers.

....

Q3 The equation on the right shows the polymerisation of ethene to form **polyethene**.

n(H H / C=C / H H) → (H H / –C–C– / H H)$_n$

many ethene molecules → polyethene

a) Draw a similar diagram in the box below to show the polymerisation of **propene** (C_3H_6).

It's easier if you think of propene as: H H / C=C / H CH_3

b) Name the polymer you have drawn. ....

Q4 Nigel has two rulers made from **different plastics**. He first tries to bend them and then he heats them. The results are shown in the table.

	RESULT ON BENDING	RESULT ON HEATING
Ruler 1	Ruler bends easily and springs back into shape	Ruler becomes soft and then melts
Ruler 2	Ruler snaps in two	Ruler doesn't soften and eventually turns black

a) Which ruler is made from a polymer that has strong forces between its molecules? ....

b) Explain why the plastic used for Ruler 1 melts and bends easily.

....

....

Polymers and Their Uses

Q1 From the list below, underline any **properties** you think it is important for a plastic to have if it is to be used to make **Wellington boots**.

low melting point waterproof rigid lightweight heat-resistant

N.B. Chlorine dissolves spandex

Q2 Complete the table to show the most suitable **use** of each polymer using the options in the list.

carrier bags kettles window frames disposable cups

POLYMER	PROPERTIES	USE
polypropene	heat-resistant	
polystyrene foam	thermal insulator	
low density polyethene	lightweight	
PVC	strong, durable, rigid	

Each use can only be used once.

Q3 Kate has three black jackets. One is made from **nylon**, another from nylon coated with **polyurethane**, and the third from a type of breathable fabric called **GORE-TEX®**.

a) Explain why the jacket coated with polyurethane would be better for Kate to wear on a rainy day than the plain nylon jacket.

....

b) Which jacket would you advise Kate to take for a week's hiking in Wales? Explain your answer.

....

....

c) The **GORE-TEX®** jacket is made from a thin film of another plastic called **expanded PTFE** laminated onto a layer of **nylon**. Explain how the two work together to give the material its useful properties.

....

....

....

Q4 Suggest a **problem** with each of the following methods of **disposing of plastics**.

a) Burial in landfill sites. ....

....

b) Burning. ....

....

c) Recycling. ....

....

Hydrocarbons — Alkanes

Q1 Look at the displayed formula of **Molecule X**, shown on the right.

```
    H   H   H
    |   |   |
H — C — C — C — H
    |   |   |
    H   H   H
```

Molecule X

a) Is molecule X a hydrocarbon? Explain your answer.

....

....

b) Give the molecular formula of molecule X.

....

c) The general formula for alkanes is C_nH_{2n+2}.
Is molecule X an alkane? Explain your answer.

....

....

d) What is the name of molecule X? ....

Q2 Hydrocarbons such as **alkanes** are held together with **covalent** bonds.

a) Tick the boxes to show if the following statements are **true** or **false**.

	True	False
i) Covalent bonds form when electrons are transferred from one atom to another.	☐	☐
ii) Covalent bonds form between atoms so that both have a full outer shell of electrons.	☐	☐
iii) Atoms can be joined by single or double covalent bonds.	☐	☐
iv) Alkanes are unsaturated compounds.	☐	☐
v) Alkanes won't form polymers.	☐	☐
vi) Ethane is an alkane molecule with a chain of four carbon atoms.	☐	☐

b) How many covalent bonds do the following atoms make?

i) Carbon .... **ii)** Hydrogen ....

Q3 The general formula for **alkanes** is C_nH_{2n+2}. Use this to write down the formulas of these alkanes.

a) pentane (5 carbons) .... **b)** hexane (6 carbons) ....

c) octane (8 carbons) .... **d)** dodecane (12 carbons) ....

Top Tip: These questions on hydrocarbons and alkanes shouldn't be too hard. Just make sure you don't confuse alkanes with alkenes — they're on the next page. Just what you wanted to hear...

Hydrocarbons — Alkenes

Q1 Complete this table showing the molecular and displayed formulas of some alkenes. If there's more than one possible displayed formula you only need to draw one correct example.

Alkene	Formula	Displayed formula
Ethene	**a)**	**b)**
c)	C_3H_6	**d)**
Butene	C_4H_8	**e)**

Q2 Tick the boxes to show if the statements are **true** or **false**?

		True	False
a)	Alkenes have double bonds between the hydrogen atoms.	☐	☐
b)	Alkenes are unsaturated.	☐	☐
c)	An unsaturated compound contains only single bonds.	☐	☐
d)	Alkenes are not very useful.	☐	☐
e)	Ethene has two carbon atoms.	☐	☐

Q3 Mark has two boiling tubes. One contains 20 cm^3 of **hexane** and the other contains 20 cm^3 of **hexene**. He also has a bottle of bromine water.

a) Describe how Mark can use the bromine water to tell the hexane and the hexene apart.

....

....

....

b) Name and describe the reaction that takes place between the hexene and the bromine water.

....

....

....

Fractional Distillation of Crude Oil

Q1 Circle the correct answer to each of the following questions.

a) Why is crude oil called a fossil fuel?

A — Because the oil is millions of years old.

B — Because the oil was formed from animals and plants buried long ago.

C — Because burning the fuel causes global warming.

b) Why is crude oil non-renewable?

A — It is impossible to create new oil.

B — Oil is very hard to find.

C — Oil is being used up faster than it is being formed.

phwoar... nice tank, love

Q2 Circle the correct words to complete these sentences.

a) Crude oil is a **mixture** / **compound** of different molecules.

b) The molecules in crude oil are all **hydrocarbons** / **carbohydrates**.

c) If crude oil were heated, the **first** / **last** fraction to be obtained would be bitumen.

d) Diesel has **larger** / **smaller** molecules than petrol.

Q3 Label this diagram of a **fractionating column** to show where these substances can be collected.

petrol **kerosene** **diesel** **oil** **bitumen**

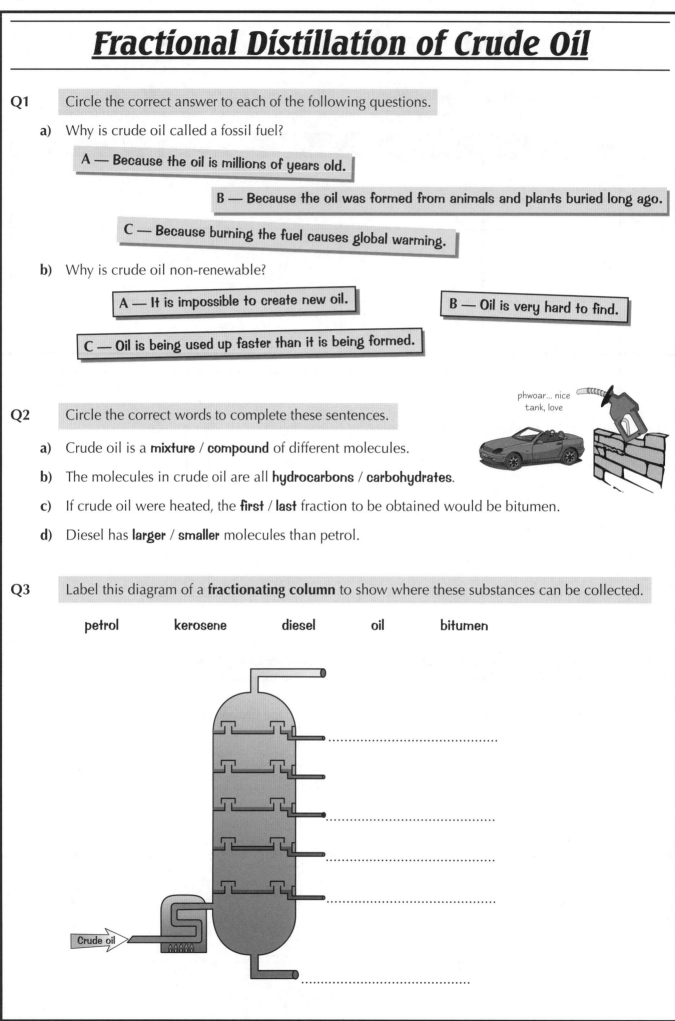

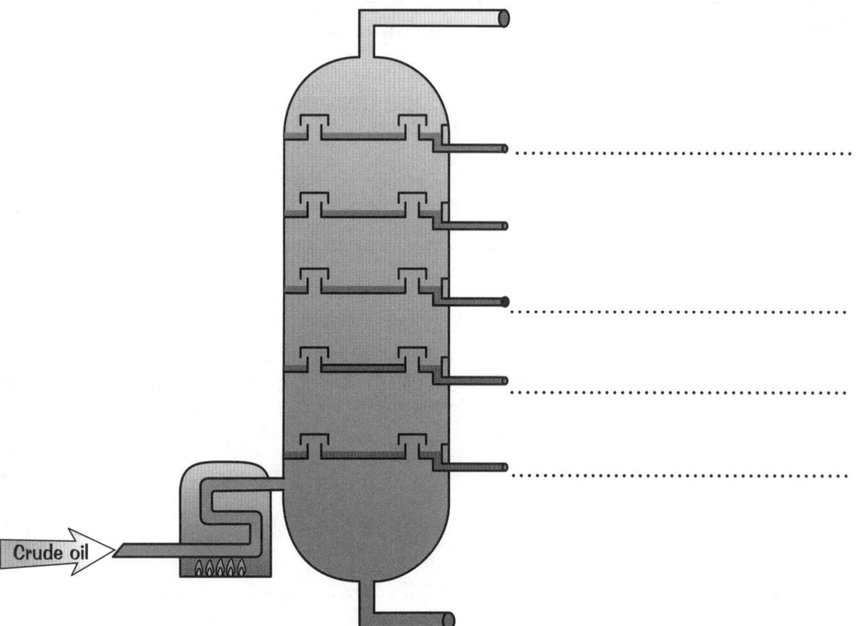
Crude oil

Fractional Distillation of Crude Oil

Q4 Crude oil is separated into different **fractions** by boiling.

a) Put these crude oil fractions into order from highest to lowest boiling point.

diesel	naphtha	kerosene	petrol

highest .... **lowest**

b) Put the same fractions in order from most to least carbon atoms in their molecules.

most .... **least**

c) Look at your answers for parts **a)** and **b)**. What is the connection between the number of carbon atoms in a molecule and its boiling point?

....

....

Q5 The following sentences describe how crude oil is separated by **fractional distillation**. Fill in the blanks in the sentences using some of the words below.

high gases cooler heated smaller low bottom hotter fractions

A Crude oil is .... causing most of the hydrocarbons to boil.

B The hot .... rise up the fractionating column.

C As they rise, the temperature begins to get ....

D Near the .... of the column, large molecules with lots of carbon atoms condense first because they have .... boiling points.

E As the gases rise further and become cooler, ... molecules with lower boiling points turn into liquids.

F In this way crude oil is separated into ...., which are mixtures of only a few different hydrocarbons, with similar numbers of carbon atoms and similar boiling points.

Top Tip: Fractional distillation can be a tricky idea to get your head round, but once you do you'll be able to answer anything they throw at you. Learn the order of the fractions too, they love that.

Hydrocarbon Properties — Bonds

Q1 During **fractional distillation** hydrocarbons are separated using their **boiling points**.

a) Explain the trend in the boiling points of alkanes in terms of **intermolecular forces**.

....

....

....

b) Explain why the hydrocarbon molecules do not breakdown into hydrogen and carbon atoms when they are heated during fractional distillation.

....

....

Q2 Here is a table showing the properties of some **alkanes**.

Alkane	Melting point (°C)	Boiling point (°C)
Methane (CH_4)	−182	−162
Pentane (C_5H_{12})	−130	36
Hexane (C_6H_{14})	−95	69
Decane ($C_{10}H_{22}$)	−30	174
Octadecane ($C_{18}H_{38}$)	28	317

a) Which of these alkanes are liquids at room temperature (25 °C)?

....

b) Which of these liquids is the most volatile? ....

c) Which alkane will be a solid at room temperature? ....

d) Which of the liquids will flow most easily along a pipe? ....

Q3 Jim investigated how the **size** of a hydrocarbon molecule affects its **volatility**. He took 50 cm^3 of each of three different hydrocarbons and put them into evaporating basins. He left them for five hours and then measured how much of each was left. His results are shown in the table below.

No. of C atoms	Initial vol. (cm^3)	Vol. after 5 hours (cm^3)	Vol. lost (cm^3)
6	50	8	
10	50	37	
12	50	48	

a) Complete the table by filling in the volume of each hydrocarbon that has evaporated.

b) If this is to be a fair test, what must be kept the same for all three hydrocarbons (apart from using the same volume of each)?

Think what could affect how fast the liquids evaporate.

....

c) What can Jim conclude about volatility and the size of hydrocarbons?

....

....

Cracking

Q1 Fill in the gaps using the words below.

high	shorter	longer	catalyst	cracking	diesel	low	molecules	petrol

There is more need for .... chain fractions of crude oil such as .... than for .... chain fractions such as .... Heating long hydrocarbon molecules to .... temperatures with a .... breaks them down into smaller .... This is called ....

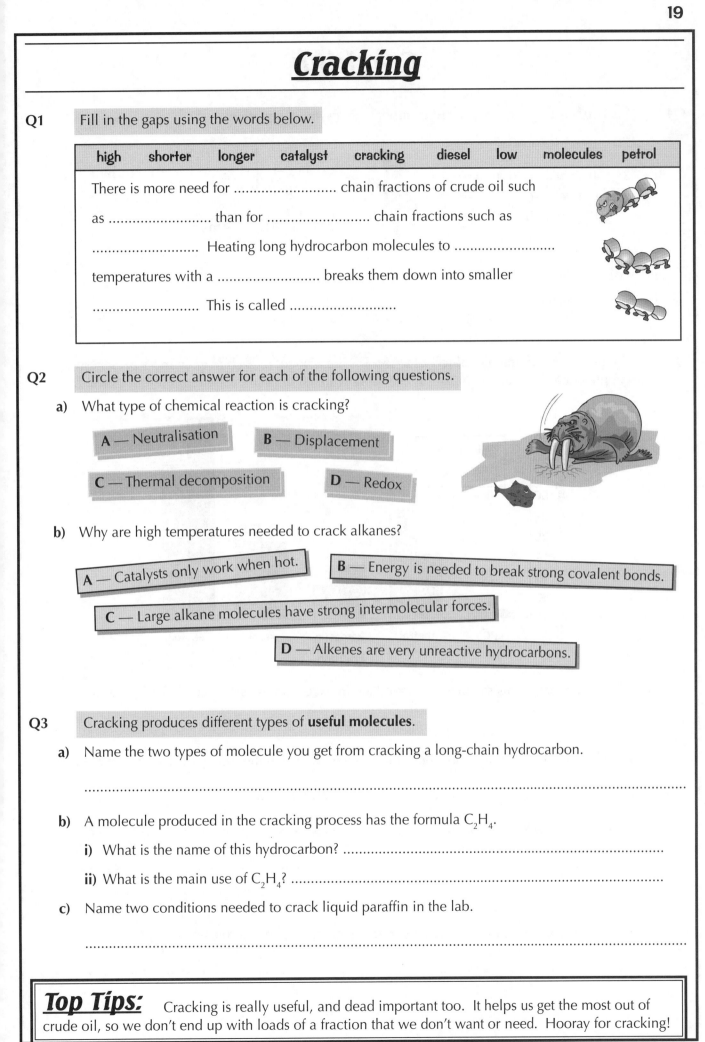

Q2 Circle the correct answer for each of the following questions.

a) What type of chemical reaction is cracking?

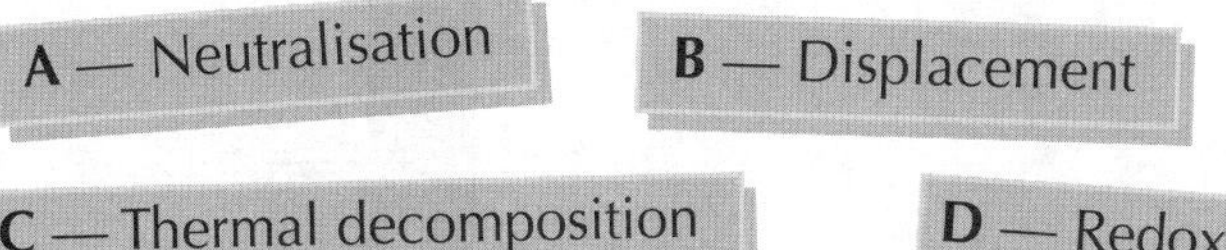

A — Neutralisation

B — Displacement

C — Thermal decomposition

D — Redox

b) Why are high temperatures needed to crack alkanes?

A — Catalysts only work when hot.

B — Energy is needed to break strong covalent bonds.

C — Large alkane molecules have strong intermolecular forces.

D — Alkenes are very unreactive hydrocarbons.

Q3 Cracking produces different types of **useful molecules**.

a) Name the two types of molecule you get from cracking a long-chain hydrocarbon.

....

b) A molecule produced in the cracking process has the formula C_2H_4.

i) What is the name of this hydrocarbon? ....

ii) What is the main use of C_2H_4? ....

c) Name two conditions needed to crack liquid paraffin in the lab.

....

Top Tips: Cracking is really useful, and dead important too. It helps us get the most out of crude oil, so we don't end up with loads of a fraction that we don't want or need. Hooray for cracking!

Cracking

Q4 Change this diagram into a **word equation** and a **symbol equation**.

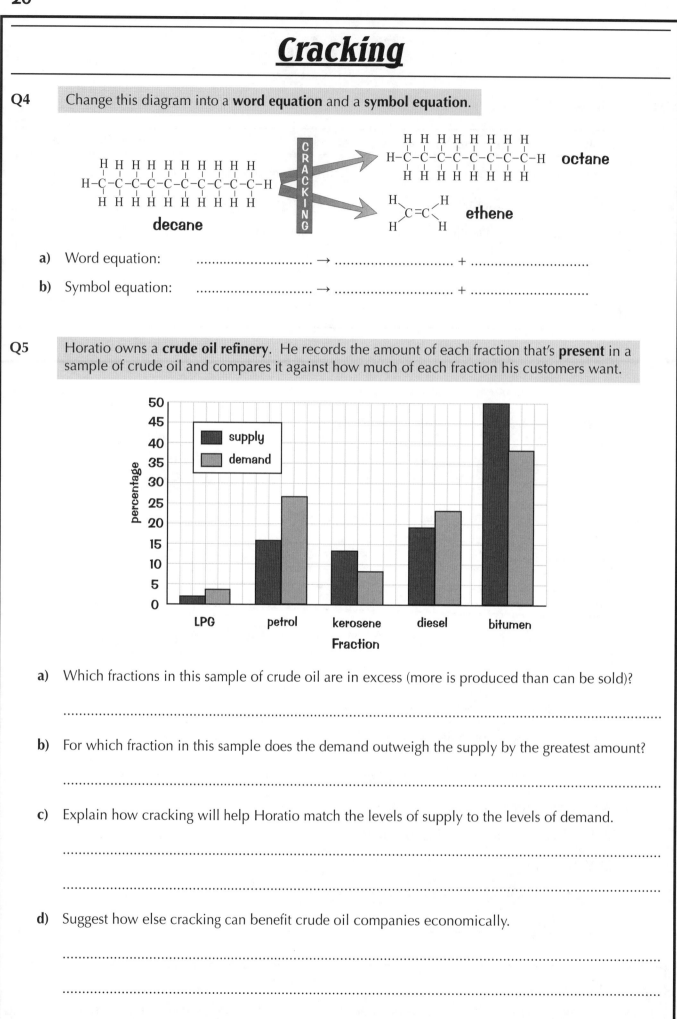

decane → CRACKING → octane + ethene

a) Word equation: .... → .... + ...

b) Symbol equation: .... → .... + ...

Q5 Horatio owns a **crude oil refinery**. He records the amount of each fraction that's **present** in a sample of crude oil and compares it against how much of each fraction his customers want.

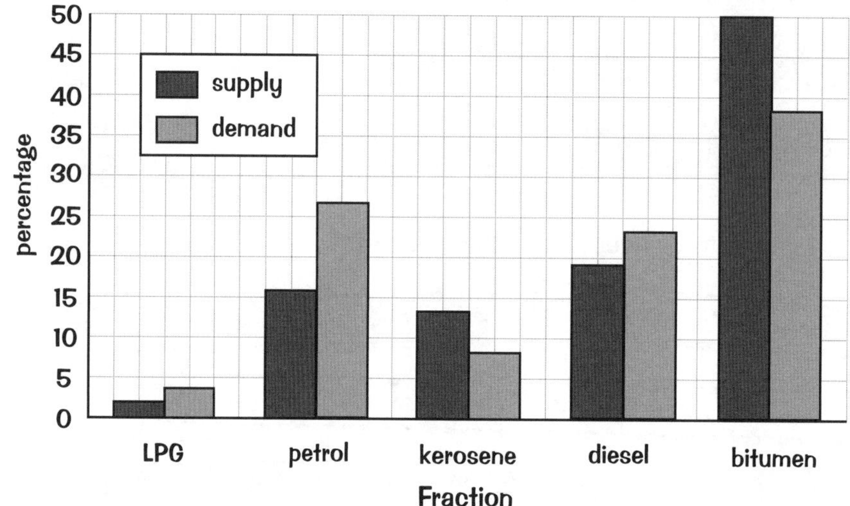

a) Which fractions in this sample of crude oil are in excess (more is produced than can be sold)?

....

b) For which fraction in this sample does the demand outweigh the supply by the greatest amount?

....

c) Explain how cracking will help Horatio match the levels of supply to the levels of demand.

....

....

d) Suggest how else cracking can benefit crude oil companies economically.

....

....

Use of Fossil Fuels

Q1 Circle the correct words to complete the passage below.

We rely on crude oil to provide us with **energy / metals** and as a source of raw materials for making chemicals. Because crude oil is a **renewable / non-renewable** resource it will eventually run out. As it becomes scarcer the price of oil will **increase / decrease** and everything that relies on oil as a raw material or fuel for its production will become **more expensive / cheaper**.

Q2 The amount of fossil fuels being burnt worldwide is **increasing** every year.

a) Give one reason why the amount of fossil fuels being burnt is increasing.

....

b) Some countries only have very small reserves of fossil fuels.
Describe the political problems associated with having to import oil.

....

....

....

Q3 Complete the passage using some of the words given below.

detergents field waterproof cold slick absorbent heat toxic coagulants

If a tanker carrying crude oil is damaged the oil spills into the sea creating an oil ....

If any of this oil gets onto the feathers of seabirds it stops them from being ....

Birds that are contaminated in this way often die of ....

Sometimes .... are added to spilled oil in an attempt to disperse it, but these can be .... to marine wildlife, like fish and shellfish.

Q4 Isobella is trying to decide which hydrocarbon, A or B, is the best one to use as a fuel. She tests the **energy content** of the hydrocarbons by using them to heat 50 cm^3 of water from 25 °C to 40 °C. The results of this experiment are shown in the table.

Hydrocarbon	Initial Mass (g)	Final Mass (g)	Mass of Fuel Burnt (g)
A	98	92	
B	102	89	

a) Complete the table by calculating the mass of fuel that was burned in each case.

b) Which fuel contains more energy per gram? ....

c) Name two other things Isobella should consider when choosing the best fuel to use.

....

Burning Fuels

Q1 Hydrocarbons make good **fuels.**

a) Write a **general word equation** for completely burning a hydrocarbon in the open air.

....

b) Write **balanced symbol equations** for completely burning these alkanes in open air:

i) methane, CH_4 ....

ii) propane, C_3H_8 ....

Q2 Describe how the apparatus on the right could be used to show that water and carbon dioxide are produced when **hexane** (a hydrocarbon) is completely burned.

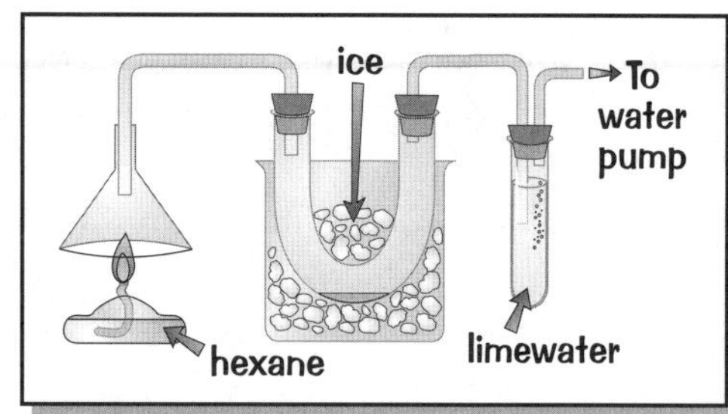

....

....

....

....

Q3 **Incomplete combustion** can cause problems.

a) Does **complete** or **incomplete** combustion release more energy?

....

b) Complete the balanced symbol equations for the incomplete combustion of butane:

i) to produce carbon monoxide.

$2\ C_4H_{10}$ + ... → .... H_2O + ... CO

ii) to produce carbon.

$2\ C_4H_{10}$ + ... → .... H_2O + ... C

c) Why is incomplete combustion:

i) dangerous? ....

ii) a waste of fuel? ....

iii) messy? ....

The Evolution of the Atmosphere

Q1 Tick the boxes next to the sentences below that are **true**.

When the Earth was formed, its surface was molten. ☐

The Earth's early atmosphere is thought to have been mostly oxygen. ☐

When oxygen started building up in the atmosphere, all organisms began to thrive. ☐

The early atmosphere was mostly made up of gases that had escaped from inside the Earth during volcanic eruptions. ☐

Q2 The amount of **carbon dioxide** in the atmosphere has changed over the last 4.5 billion or so years.

Describe how the level of carbon dioxide has changed and explain why this change happened.

....

....

....

....

Q3 Draw lines to put the statements in the **right order** on the timeline. One has been done for you.

Present

NOT TO SCALE

4500 million years ago

The Earth cooled down slightly. A thin crust formed.

Water vapour condensed to form oceans.

The Earth formed. There was lots of volcanic activity.

More complex organisms evolved.

Plant life appeared.

The atmosphere is about four-fifths nitrogen and one-fifth oxygen.

Oxygen builds up in the air as plants photosynthesise.

Don't get confused — 4500 million is the same as 4.5 billion.

The Evolution of the Atmosphere

Q4 The pie chart below shows the proportions of different gases in the Earth's atmosphere today.

a) Add the labels '**Nitrogen**', '**Oxygen**', and '**Carbon dioxide and other gases**'.

Earth's Atmosphere Today

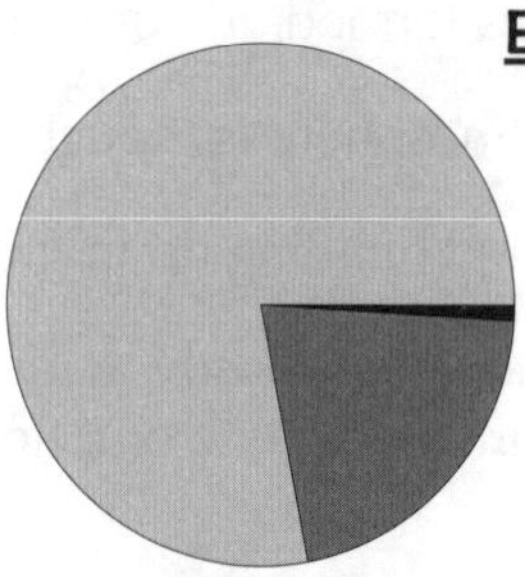

b) Give the approximate percentages of the following gases in the air today:

Nitrogen ....

Oxygen ....

Carbon dioxide ....

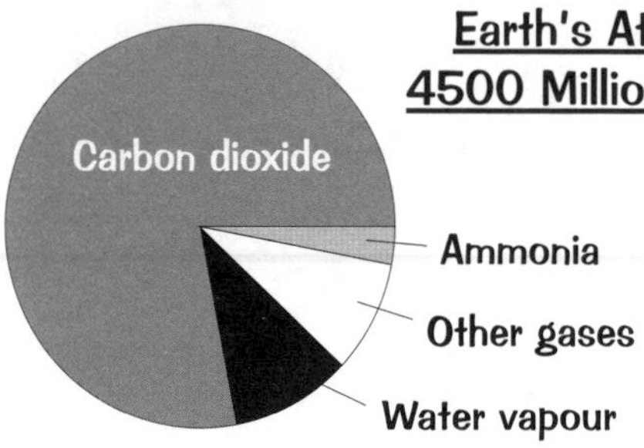

c) This pie chart shows the proportions of different gases that we think were in the Earth's atmosphere 4500 million years ago.

Earth's Atmosphere 4500 Million Years Ago

Carbon dioxide

Ammonia

Other gases

Water vapour

Describe the main differences between today's atmosphere and the atmosphere 4500 million years ago.

....

....

d) Explain why the amount of water vapour has decreased.

....

....

What did the water vapour change into?

e) Explain how oxygen was introduced into the atmosphere.

....

f) Give two effects of the oxygen levels in the atmosphere rising.

1. ....

....

2. ....

....

g) Explain why the percentage of nitrogen gas in the air has increased so much.

....

....

....

The Carbon Cycle

Q1 Here is a diagram of the **carbon cycle**.

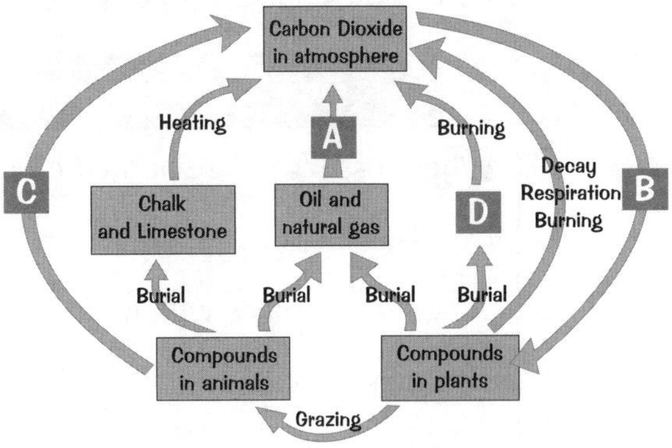

Carbon Dioxide in atmosphere
Heating
Burning
A
C
Chalk and Limestone
Oil and natural gas
D
Decay
Respiration
Burning
B
Burial
Burial
Burial
Burial
Compounds in animals
Compounds in plants
Grazing

a) What is process A? ....

b) What is process B? ....

c) Process C could be decay. What else could it be?

....

d) What is substance D? ....

Q2 The **human population** is increasing rapidly and this increase is affecting the atmosphere.

List two reasons why this dramatic increase in population has caused a rise in CO_2 levels.

....

....

Sid's day

8.00 am: Wakes up, fills his kettle to the top and makes a cup of tea to enjoy with a pineapple, which was grown in Ghana.
10.00 am: Drives to the travel agent in his shiny new 4X4 car and books a holiday in Hawaii departing that evening.
11.00 am: Goes shopping for a grass skirt.
11.30 am: Returns home and decides to put on his grass skirt. But it's a bit chilly, so he puts the heating on high.
5.00 pm: Leaves for the airport, leaving all the lights on to keep burglars away.

Q3 On the left is some information about what Sid does one day.

Suggest three ways that Sid could have lowered the amount of carbon dioxide he produced.

....

....

....

....

Q4 **Deforestation** increases the amount of **carbon dioxide** released into the atmosphere and decreases the amount removed.

a) Give two reasons why deforestation causes carbon dioxide to be added to the atmosphere.

....

....

b) Why does deforestation reduce the amount of CO_2 removed from the atmosphere?

....

Top Tips: It's tough minimising your carbon emissions when you live in a world of cheap flights, abundant plastic bags, supermarkets filled with cheap exotic food, and central heating. But if we carry on the way we're going, the world's likely to be in a lot of trouble one day.

Air Pollution and Acid Rain

Q1 Use the words and phrases below to complete the paragraph.

nitric   global warming   sulfuric   nitrogen oxides   acid rain

When fossil fuels are burned carbon dioxide is produced. The main problem caused by this is .... The gas sulfur dioxide is also produced. When it combines with moisture in the air .... acid is produced. This falls as acid rain. In the high temperatures inside a car engine nitrogen and oxygen from the air react together to produce .... These react with moisture to make .... acid, which is another cause of acid rain.

Q2 **Pollutants** from burning fossil fuels cause a variety of problems.

a) Why might architects choose **not** to build from limestone in polluted cities?

....

b) Give **two** other consequences of acid rain.

....

c) Briefly describe how photochemical smog is formed.

....

....

Q3 **Catalytic converters** reduce the amount of harmful gases that are released into the atmosphere.

a) Complete the following equations to show a reaction that occurs in a catalytic converter:

i) carbon monoxide + nitrogen oxide → .... + ...

ii) ....CO + ...NO → .... + ...

b) What catalyst is usually used for this reaction? ....

c) Why is carbon monoxide so dangerous?

....

....

Mixed Questions — Module C1

Q1 **Baking powder** is often one of the ingredients in cakes.

a) Baking powder contains sodium hydrogen carbonate.

i) Sodium hydrogen carbonate can be produced by reacting soda ash with water and carbon dioxide. Balance the equation below that shows this process.

.... Na_2CO_3 + ... CO_2 + ... H_2O → .... $NaHCO_3$

ii) Explain why sodium hydrogen carbonate is a useful addition to a cake mix.

....

....

b) The cake mix fills the bottom of the tin that it is poured into, but when cooked, the cake no longer flows. Explain why this is in terms of the **movement** of the particles and the **forces** between them.

....

....

Q2 **Chloroethene** (C_2H_3Cl) is used to make the addition polymer, **polychloroethene** (**PVC**).

a) Chloroethene is produced from ethene. Ethene is commonly made by thermal decomposition of long-chain hydrocarbons. What is the name for this process?

....

b) What feature does chloroethene have that allows it to form an addition polymer?

....

c) Write an equation in the space on the right for the polymerisation of chloroethene, using **displayed formulae** to show the structure of chloroethene and the repeating unit in PVC.

d) PVC can be used to make plastic pipes and guttering.
Suggest **two** properties that a plastic should have if it is going to be used to make guttering.

....

e) PVC is **non-biodegradable**.

i) Explain what this means.

....

ii) Suggest why chemists are working to produce polymers that do biodegrade.

....

Mixed Questions — Module C1

Q3 Nail varnish does **not** dissolve in water. This is important, otherwise every time a person washed their hands it would wash away.

a) Explain, in terms of the molecules, why nail varnish does not dissolve in water.

....

b) Explain, in terms of the molecules, how nail varnish remover removes the varnish.

....

c) The active chemical in nail varnish is a **volatile liquid**.

i) Explain what "**volatile**" means.

....

ii) Explain, in terms of the particles, what happens when this chemical **evaporates** from the nails.

....

....

iii) Name **another product** that must be **volatile** in order to work effectively. Explain why this is.

....

....

Q4 **Fuel X** is a hydrocarbon that can be burnt to release energy.
A company is trying to decide whether or not to use fuel X to power its machinery.

a) Give two properties of fuel X, other than its energy value, that the company should take into account when deciding whether or not to use it industrially.

1. ....

2. ....

b) Fuel X contains only hydrogen and carbon.
What could the products of the reaction include when fuel X is burnt:

i) in plentiful oxygen ....

ii) in low oxygen ....

c) A research scientist at the company burns a small quantity of the fuel to determine its energy value. If he burns it in a plentiful supply of oxygen, what colour will the flame be?

....

Mixed Questions — Module C1

Q5 Crude oil is a mixture of hydrocarbons, which is separated by **fractional distillation** into useful fractions.

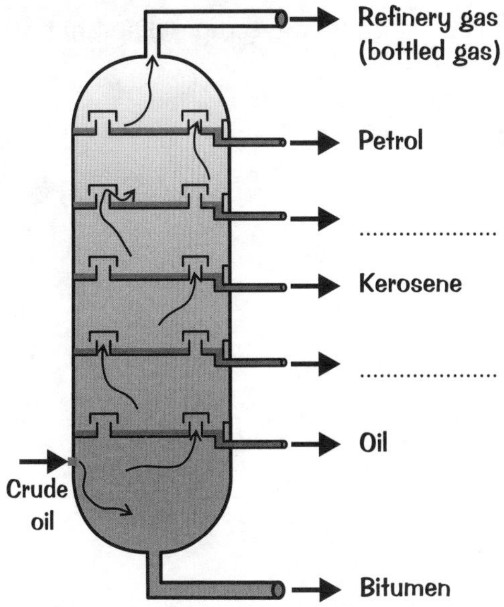

a) **i)** Label the **diesel** and **naphtha** fractions on the diagram.

ii) Which fraction has the higher boiling point? Underline the correct answer.

naphtha **diesel**

iii) Why does this fraction have a higher boiling point?

....

....

....

b) Explain how the fractions are separated in fractional distillation.

....

....

c) Explain why plastic products may become much more expensive in the future.

....

....

Q6 The atmosphere of Mars consists of 95.3% carbon dioxide, 2.7% nitrogen, and 2% of other gases.

a) Describe the similarities between this and the early atmosphere of Earth.

....

....

b) Describe the differences between the compositions of the atmospheres of Mars and Earth today.

....

....

c) Describe how human activity is affecting the composition of the air.

....

....

....

The Earth's Structure

Q1 **Label** this simple diagram of the Earth's interior.

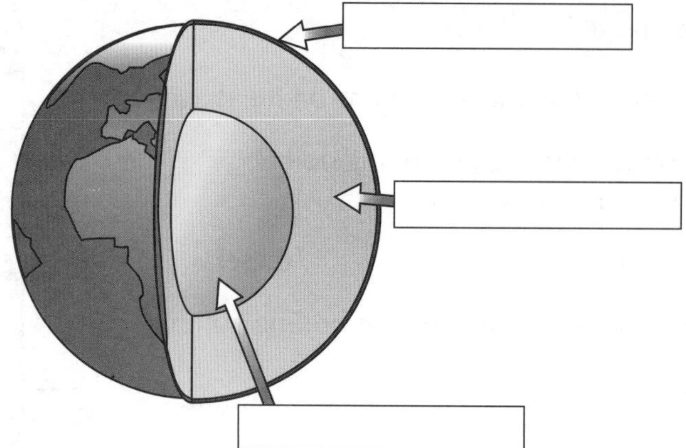

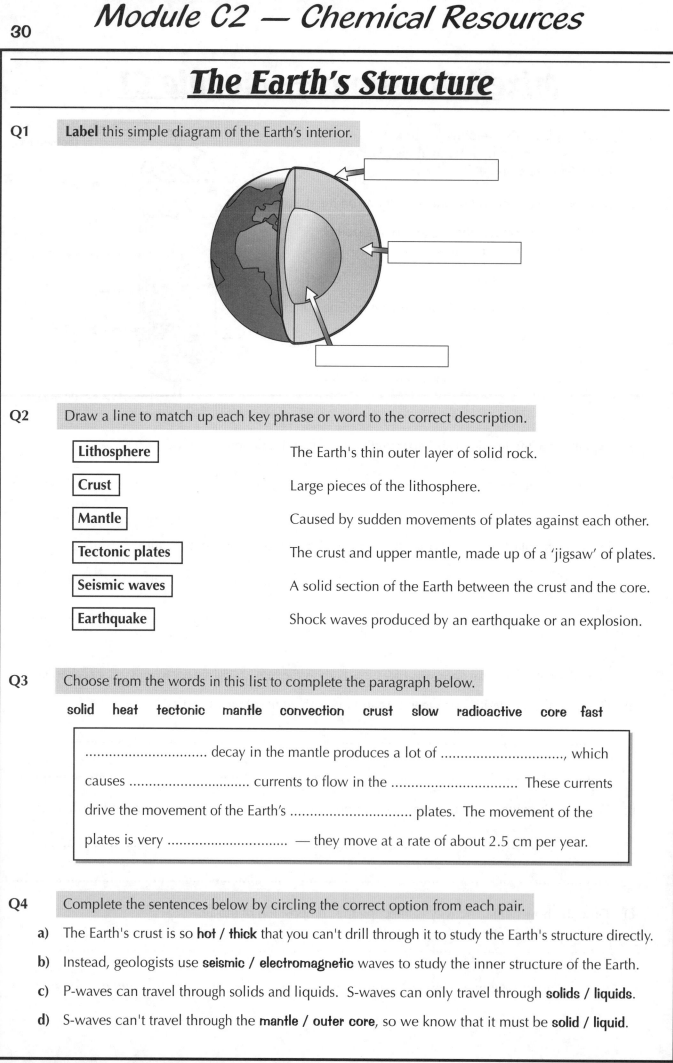

Q2 Draw a line to match up each key phrase or word to the correct description.

Lithosphere	The Earth's thin outer layer of solid rock.
Crust	Large pieces of the lithosphere.
Mantle	Caused by sudden movements of plates against each other.
Tectonic plates	The crust and upper mantle, made up of a 'jigsaw' of plates.
Seismic waves	A solid section of the Earth between the crust and the core.
Earthquake	Shock waves produced by an earthquake or an explosion.

Q3 Choose from the words in this list to complete the paragraph below.

solid heat tectonic mantle convection crust slow radioactive core fast

.... decay in the mantle produces a lot of ...., which causes .... currents to flow in the .... These currents drive the movement of the Earth's .... plates. The movement of the plates is very .... — they move at a rate of about 2.5 cm per year.

Q4 Complete the sentences below by circling the correct option from each pair.

a) The Earth's crust is so **hot / thick** that you can't drill through it to study the Earth's structure directly.

b) Instead, geologists use **seismic / electromagnetic** waves to study the inner structure of the Earth.

c) P-waves can travel through solids and liquids. S-waves can only travel through **solids / liquids**.

d) S-waves can't travel through the **mantle / outer core**, so we know that it must be **solid / liquid**.

The Earth's Structure

Q5 Look at the diagram showing the boundary between two tectonic plates.

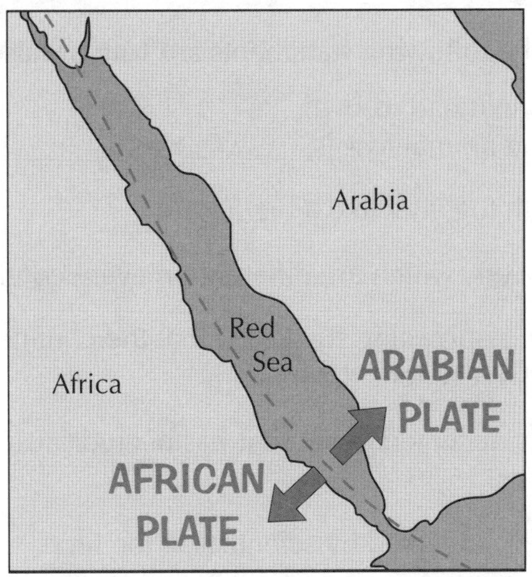

Remember to include a unit in your answer.

The Red Sea is widening at a speed of 1.6 cm per year.

a) If the sea level remains the same, how much will the Red Sea widen in 10 000 years?

b) The Red Sea is currently exactly 325 km wide at a certain point. If the sea level remains the same, how wide will the Red Sea be at this point in 20 000 years' time?

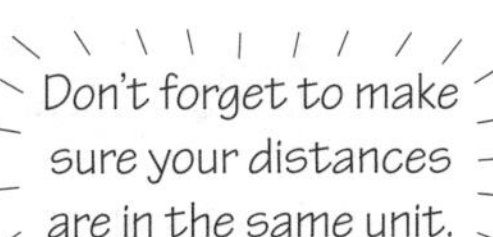

Don't forget to make sure your distances are in the same unit.

Q6 The map below on the left shows where most of the world's earthquakes take place.

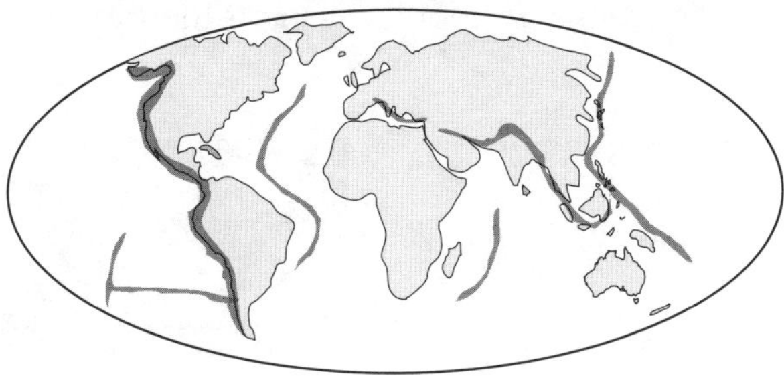

= main earthquake zones

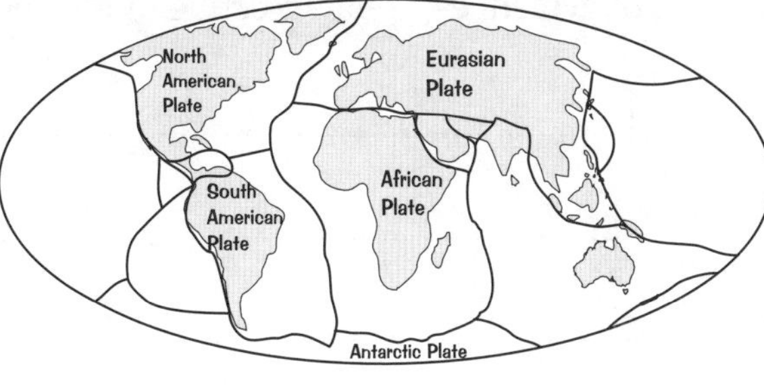

Compare this map to the one showing the tectonic plates.
What do you notice about the main earthquake zones?

Plate Tectonics

Q1 Wegener studied astronomy at Berlin University in 1904. His fascination with observing identical fossils on both sides of the Atlantic led him to produce his theory of **continental drift** in 1914.

Tick the boxes to say whether the following statements are **true** or **false**.

		True	False
a)	Wegener found that each continent had its own unrelated collection of plant and animal fossils.	☐	☐
b)	The Earth's continents seem to fit together like a big jigsaw.	☐	☐
c)	Rock formations are made of layers, which are different on every continent.	☐	☐
d)	The discovery that the sea floor is spreading suggested that the continents are moving apart. This supports Wegener's theory.	☐	☐
e)	Wegener's theory is now widely accepted because it has been discussed and tested by a range of scientists.	☐	☐
f)	Wegener's theory was **not** readily accepted by scientists at the time.	☐	☐

Q2 Use the words below to complete the passage about Wegener's theory of continental drift.

thousand **countries** **tectonics** **million** **Alfred** **continents** **movement** **Pangaea**

Wegener suggested that 300 .... years ago there was one supercontinent, called .... This supercontinent broke up into smaller chunks — our modern day .... These chunks are still moving apart. He called his idea the theory of continental drift. It is the basis of the modern theory of plate ....

Q3 Wegener's theory is now accepted by scientists because it explains lots of different pieces of **evidence**. Briefly describe three pieces of evidence that support Wegener's theory.

1. ....

....

....

2. ....

....

3. ....

....

Volcanic Eruptions

Q1 Number these processes in the correct order to explain **how volcanoes may form.**

- [ ] Magma rises up through the dense crust to the surface, forming a volcano.
- [ ] The denser oceanic crust is forced underground (subduction).
- [ ] Continental crust and oceanic crust collide.
- [ ] Rock melts underground, forming magma.

Q2 Imagine you live near an active volcano. This volcano only produces **iron-rich basalt** magma.

a) Describe the type of lava produced from iron-rich basalt magma.

....

b) Why would it be much more dangerous living near a volcano that produces **silica-rich rhyolite**?

....

Q3 Geologists study volcanoes to try to predict how likely they are to **erupt** in the future.

a) Describe one sign that might suggest that a volcano is going to erupt.

....

....

b) Which of the following statements about volcanic eruptions is true? Circle the correct answer.

A — Thanks to past studies, geologists can now say for certain exactly when a volcano will erupt.

B — Geologists cannot say for certain that a volcano is about to erupt, but can often tell if an eruption is likely to happen.

C — Geologists can now predict how likely a volcano is to erupt, but not as accurately as they used to be able to.

Top Tips: There are no end of problems with predicting volcanic eruptions. There are likely to be loads of people living near a volcano — it'd be impossible to evacuate them all every time scientists thought there might possibly be an eruption some time soon. It just wouldn't work.

The Three Different Types of Rock

Q1 There are three **main types** of rock.

a) Join up each **rock type** with the correct **method of formation**.

ROCK TYPE	METHOD OF FORMATION
igneous rocks	formed from layers of sediment
sedimentary rocks	formed when magma cools
metamorphic rocks	formed under intense heat and pressure

b) Give an example of:

i) an igneous rock ....

ii) a sedimentary rock ....

iii) a metamorphic rock ....

Q2 Erica notices that the stonework of her local church contains tiny fragments of **sea shells**.

a) Suggest an explanation for this.

....

....

b) Describe how sedimentary rock is 'cemented' together.

....

....

c) Powdered limestone and powdered marble react with other chemicals, such as hydrochloric acid, in an identical fashion. Explain this.

....

....

Top Tips: You might think that rocks are just boring lumps of.... rock. But you'd be wrong — rocks are actually boring lumps of different kinds of rock. And the kind of rock they are depends on how they're formed — and this is the stuff you need to make sure you know.

The Three Different Types of Rock

Q3 Use the words below to complete the paragraph.

heat metamorphic igneous crystals texture magma sedimentary

.... rock forms from layers of sediment compacted at the bottom of seas over millions of years. As layers build up, the older rock is subjected to .... and pressure. This can change the .... and mineral structure of the rock and is how .... rocks form. If the rock gets too hot it melts and is then known as .... This can force its way to the surface and cool to become .... rock. These rocks contain minerals in the form of ....

Q4 Below are the processes involved in the formation of **marble**.

a) Number the boxes to show the order in which they occur.

- ☐ Heat and pressure causes limestone to change into marble.
- ☐ Dead sea creatures become buried in sediment.
- ☐ Sea creatures die.
- ☐ Natural mineral cement sticks the sediment together and limestone forms.
- ☐ Several layers of sediment build up and compress the lower layers.

b) Describe the differences between limestone and marble.

....

....

c) Marble is a **metamorphic** rock, and granite is an **igneous** rock. Which is harder?

....

Q5 Calcium carbonate can undergo **thermal decomposition**.

a) Explain what thermal decomposition means.

....

....

b) Write out the word and symbol equations for the thermal decomposition of calcium carbonate.

Word equation: ....

Symbol equation: ....

Construction Materials

Q1 Match each **construction material** to the **raw materials** that are needed to make it.

CONSTRUCTION MATERIALS	RAW MATERIALS
cement	ores
bricks	limestone
iron	sand
aluminium	clay
concrete	gravel

Some construction materials are made from more than one raw material from the list.

Q2 Choose from the words below to complete the paragraphs.

clay sodium carbonate cement calcium carbonate silicon dioxide
melting extracting aluminium fired bricks soda

a) Glass is made by .... limestone (...), sand (...) and soda (...), then cooling the mixture.

b) When moist, ... is a mouldable material made from decomposed rock. If it is .... at high temperature it can be made into ....

c) Powdered limestone can also be mixed with ...., then roasted in a kiln to make ....

Q3 Reinforced concrete is called a '**composite material**'.

a) Explain why this is. ....

b) Explain why reinforced concrete is a better construction material than normal concrete.

....

Q4 Quarrying limestone can cause a variety of **problems**.

Describe three environmental problems caused by quarrying.

1. ....

2. ....

3. ....

Extracting Pure Copper

Q1 Copper is found in the ground in **ores** such as **chalcopyrite**.

a) How might copper be **extracted** from its ore? ....

b) What is used as the **anode** during the purification of copper by electrolysis?

....

c) Explain how copper is transferred from the anode to the cathode during electrolysis.

....

....

....

Q2 The diagram below shows the purification of copper by electrolysis.

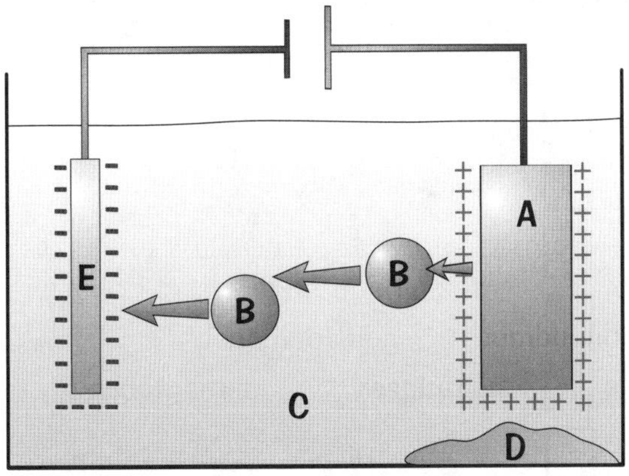

Write the labels that should go at points A–E:

A ....

B ....

C ....

D ....

E ....

Q3 When copper is purified by electrolysis, a **reduction reaction** takes place at the **cathode**, and an **oxidation reaction** happens at the **anode**.

a) Write half-equations for the purification of copper by electrolysis.

i) Cathode: ....

ii) Anode: ....

b) Complete the definition of **reduction** by circling the correct word from each pair:

A reduction reaction is one where a substance **gains / loses** electrons or **gains / loses** oxygen.

Q4 Tick the boxes to show which of the following are good reasons for **recycling copper**.

- [ ] It's cheaper than mining new copper.
- [ ] It uses less energy and therefore less fossil fuel.
- [ ] You obtain a higher quality of copper.
- [ ] It doesn't take much effort.

Alloys

Q1 Choose from the words below to complete the paragraph.

sulfur	carbon	bronze	non-metal	alloy	brass	gas

If you mix a metal with another element the resulting mixture is called an .... The other element may be a ....

An example of this is steel where iron is mixed with small amounts of .... Alternatively, the other element could be another metal.

An example of this is .... where copper is combined with zinc.

Q2 Metals are mixed with other elements to give them different properties for different uses.

a) Tick the correct boxes to show whether each statement is **true** or **false**.

	True	False
i) Bronze is made of copper and tin.	☐	☐
ii) Steel contains copper.	☐	☐
iii) Nitinol is made of silver and nickel.	☐	☐
iv) Amalgam contains mercury.	☐	☐
v) Brass contains zinc.	☐	☐
vi) Solder contains aluminium.	☐	☐
vii) Brass contains carbon.	☐	☐

b) Draw lines to join up the following alloys with their uses.

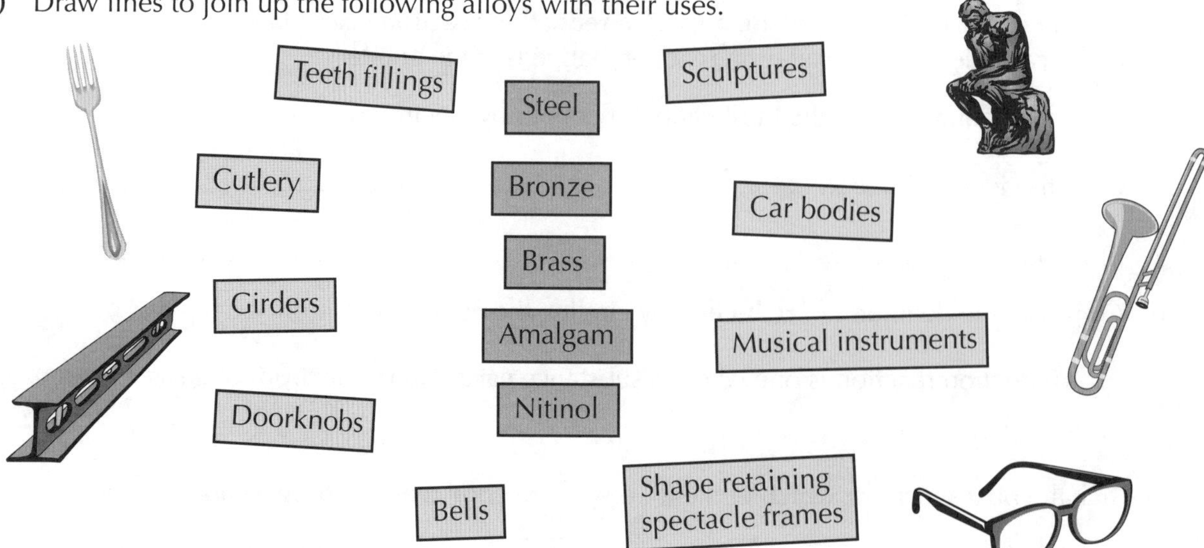

Alloys

Q3 The table below shows three types of **bronze** alloy. These alloys only contain tin and copper.

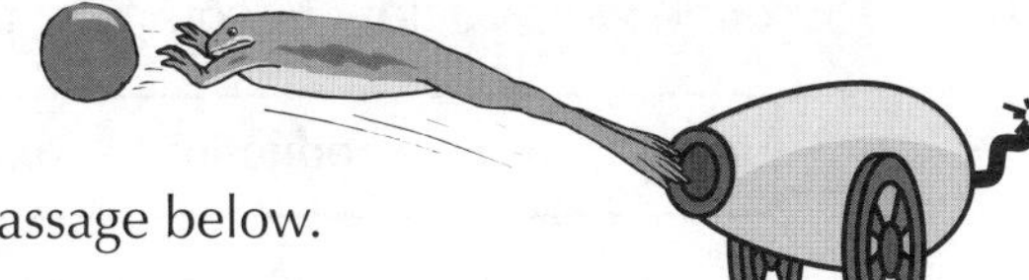

a) Circle the correct words in each pair to complete the passage below.

> Bronze is much **softer** / **harder** and **stronger** / **weaker** than tin.
> It's also **more** / **less** resistant to corrosion than either copper or tin.

b) What is the % of copper in **commercial bronze**?

....

c) What type of bronze do you think is most likely to be used for gold decorations?

....

Alloy	% tin	% copper	Appearance
Hi-Tin Bronze	20	80	Silver
Commercial bronze	10		Dark orange
Hi-copper bronze	5	95	Gold

Q4 Different alloys have different **advantages** and **disadvantages**.

a) Give one disadvantage of **quick-solidifying solder**.

....

b) If you could make car bodies from **nitinol**, what advantage would this have?

....

....

....

Think about how easy it would be to repair after a minor crash.

c) Suggest a physical property that would make a **brass** screw better than a copper screw.

....

d) Why are you much more likely to see an outdoor sculpture made of **bronze** than of copper or tin?

....

e) What property of steel makes it more suitable than iron for:

i) drill bits. ....

ii) ships. ....

Top Tips: The properties of an alloy determine what it's used for, e.g. if you want an alloy that's strong, but lightweight and will harden over time, then a great solution is duralumin (which is aluminium with 4% copper, 1% manganese and some magnesium).

Building Cars

Q1 Use the words below to complete the paragraph.

salty **iron** **reduction** **oxidation** **iron(II) oxide** **iron(III) oxide** **rusting** **water**

.... is the corrosion of .... If unprotected iron comes into contact with oxygen and ...., a chemical reaction happens. Oxygen reacts with iron to produce hydrated ...., also known as rust. This is known as an .... reaction. This reaction is speeded up if the water is acidic or ....

Q2 In the table below list an advantage and a disadvantage of using **aluminium** and **steel** to make car bodies.

	Steel	**Aluminium**
Advantage		
Disadvantage		

Q3 Fill in the missing labels on the diagram using the words and phrases below. You don't have to use all the words and phrases.

Materials:
Plastic
Copper
Glass
Iron
Natural and synthetic fibres

Advantages:
Light and hard wearing
Strong, easily welded
Electrical conductor
Transparent

Dashboard
Material:
Advantage:

Windows
Material:
Advantage:

Seats
Material:
Advantage:

Electrical wiring
Material:
Advantage:

Q4 Which of the following statements are **true** and which are **false**?

		True	False
a)	Cars are recycled to save natural resources and to reduce landfill use.	☐	☐
b)	There are no laws stating how much of a new car must be recyclable.	☐	☐
c)	It's easy to separate out the non-metal bits of a car.	☐	☐
d)	Currently, scrap metal is the main component of cars that is recycled.	☐	☐

Acids and Bases

Q1 Define the following terms.

a) Acid ....

b) Base ....

c) Alkali ....

Q2 Draw lines to match the substances below to their **universal indicator colour**, **pH** value and **acid/base strength**.

	SUBSTANCE	UNIVERSAL INDICATOR COLOUR	PH	ACID/BASE STRENGTH
a)	distilled water	purple	5/6	strong alkali
b)	rainwater	yellow	8/9	weak alkali
c)	caustic soda	dark green/blue	14	weak acid
d)	washing-up liquid	red	7	neutral
e)	car battery acid	pale green	1	strong acid

Q3 a) Which is the correct word equation for a **neutralisation reaction**? Circle your answer.

salt + acid → base + water   acid + base → salt + water   acid + water → base + salt

b) Which of the ions, **H^+** or **OH^-**, is found in the largest quantity in:

i) acidic solutions? ....

ii) alkaline solutions? ....

iii) a solution with a pH of 10? ....

iv) lemon juice? ....

c) Write out the equation for neutralisation in terms H^+ and OH^- ions.

....

Q4 **Indigestion** is caused by too much acid in the stomach. **Antacid tablets** contain bases which neutralise the excess acid.

Joey wanted to test whether some antacid tablets really did **neutralise acid**. He added a tablet to some hydrochloric acid, stirred it until it dissolved and tested the pH of the solution. Further tests were carried out after dissolving a second, third and fourth tablet. His results are shown in the table.

Number of Tablets	pH
0	1
1	2
2	3
3	7
4	9

a) Describe how the pH changes when antacid tablets are added to the acid.

....

b) How many tablets were needed to neutralise the acid? ....

Reactions of Acids

Q1 Fill in the blanks to complete the word equations for **acids** reacting with **metal oxides** and **metal hydroxides**.

a) hydrochloric acid + lead oxide → .... chloride + water

b) nitric acid + copper hydroxide → copper .... + water

c) sulfuric acid + zinc oxide → zinc sulfate + ...

d) hydrochloric acid + ... oxide → nickel .... + ...

e) .... acid + copper oxide → .... nitrate + ...

f) phosphoric acid + ... hydroxide → sodium .... + ...

ACID

Q2 a) Put a tick in the box next to any of the sentences below that are **true**.

i) Alkalis are bases which can't dissolve in water. ☐

ii) Acids react with metal oxides to form a salt and water. ☐

iii) Hydrogen gas is formed when an acid reacts with an alkali. ☐

iv) Salts and water are formed when acids react with metal hydroxides. ☐

v) Sodium hydroxide is an acid that dissolves in water. ☐

b) Use the formulas below to write **symbol equations** for two acid / base reactions.

H_2SO_4 H_2O H_2O CuO $NaCl$ HCl $CuSO_4$ $NaOH$

1. ....

2. ....

Q3 **Ammonia** can be neutralised by **nitric acid** to form **ammonium nitrate**.

a) Circle the correct formula for ammonia below.

NH_4NO_3 NH_4Cl NH_3 NH_2 NH_4

b) Write down the symbol equation for the reaction between ammonia and nitric acid.

....

c) How is this neutralisation reaction different from most neutralisation reactions?

....

d) Why is ammonium nitrate a particularly good fertiliser?

....

Reactions of Acids

Q4 a) Complete the following equations.

i) H_2SO_4 + ... → K_2SO_4 + $2H_2O$

ii) $2HNO_3$ + CuO → $Cu(NO_3)_2$ + ...

iii) .... + KOH → KCl + H_2O

iv) 2HCl + ... → $CuCl_2$ + H_2O

v) H_2SO_4 + 2NaOH → .... + ...

b) **Balance** the following acid/base reactions.

i) NaOH + H_2SO_4 → Na_2SO_4 + H_2O

ii) NH_3 + H_2SO_4 → $(NH_4)_2SO_4$

Q5 **Acids** react with **metal carbonates** in neutralisation reactions.

a) Complete these word equations for the reactions of metal carbonates with acids:

i) phosphoric acid + ... carbonate →

copper .... + water + ...

ii) .... acid + magnesium .... →

.... nitrate + ... + carbon dioxide

iii) sulfuric acid + lithium carbonate → .... + ...+ ....

b) Complete and balance these symbol equations for the reactions of metal carbonates with acids:

i) .... HCl + $CaCO_3$ → $CaCl_2$ + ... + CO_2

ii) H_2SO_4 + ... → Na_2SO_4 + ... + ...

iii) .... + ... → $Ca(NO_3)_2$ + H_2O + CO_2

iv) .... + Na_2CO_3 → .... NaCl + ... + ...

Top Tips: Well take my socks off and paint me blue — that's a lot of equations. But don't forget, atoms can't be made or lost during a chemical reaction and if you can remember the different products of neutralisation reactions you can work 'em all out. The clues are all there...

Fertilisers

Q1 Choose from the words to fill in the blanks below.

non-essential	sodium	proteins	growth
phosphorus	carbohydrates	previous	essential

Fertilisers are used to increase crop yield. They provide plants with .... elements needed for ...., making crops grow faster and bigger. These elements include nitrogen, ... and potassium. Fertilisers replace elements in the soil that a .... crop could have used up.

Q2 The graph shows the amount of a **fertiliser** put onto farmland between 1940 and 2000 in one area.

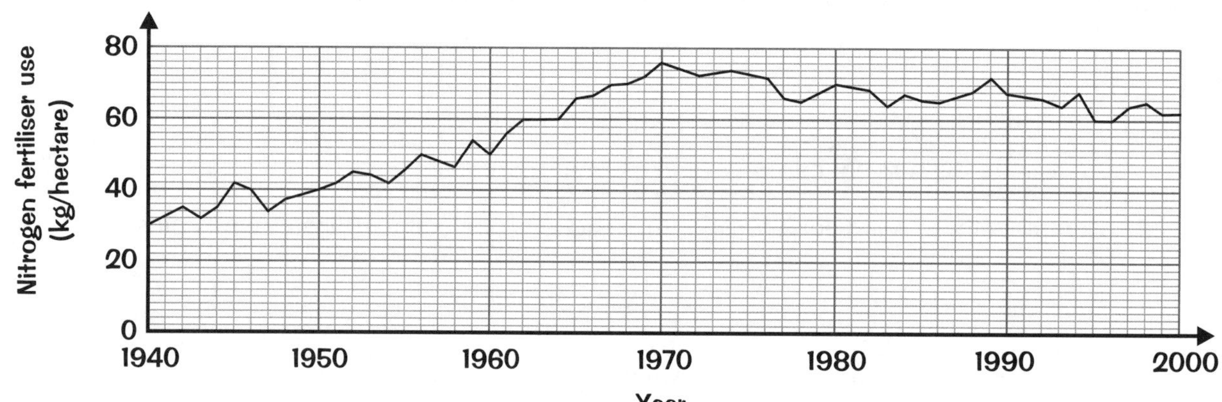

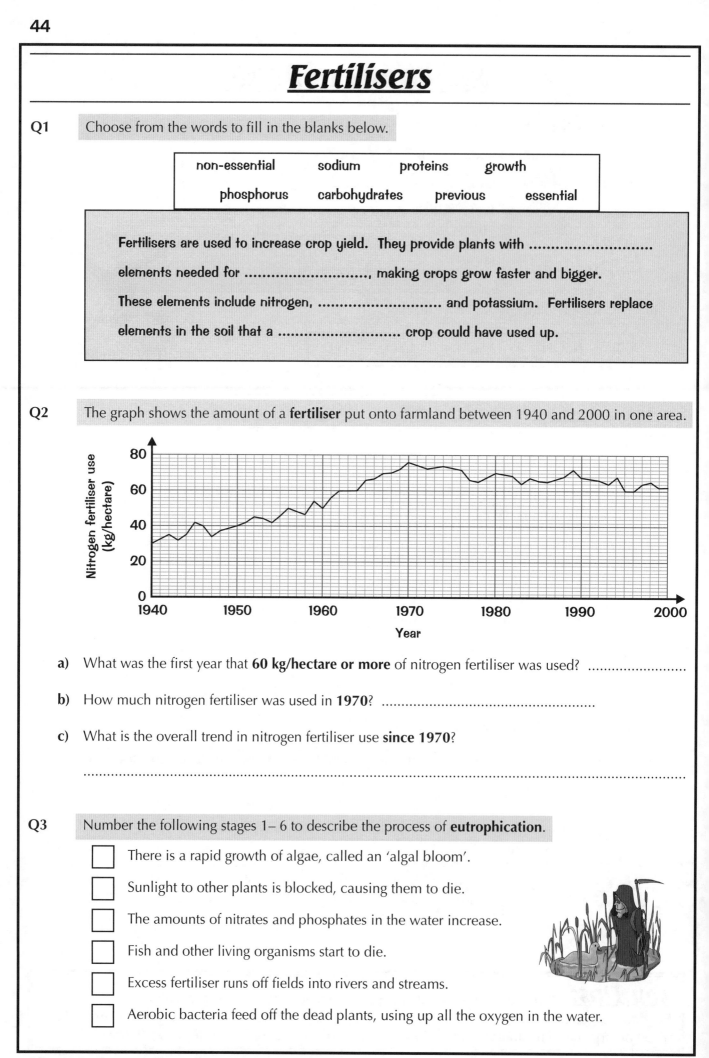

a) What was the first year that **60 kg/hectare or more** of nitrogen fertiliser was used? ....

b) How much nitrogen fertiliser was used in **1970**? ....

c) What is the overall trend in nitrogen fertiliser use **since 1970**?

....

Q3 Number the following stages 1– 6 to describe the process of **eutrophication**.

- ☐ There is a rapid growth of algae, called an 'algal bloom'.
- ☐ Sunlight to other plants is blocked, causing them to die.
- ☐ The amounts of nitrates and phosphates in the water increase.
- ☐ Fish and other living organisms start to die.
- ☐ Excess fertiliser runs off fields into rivers and streams.
- ☐ Aerobic bacteria feed off the dead plants, using up all the oxygen in the water.

Fertilisers

Q4 Sophie is concerned about the amount of **fertiliser** that gets washed into **rivers**.

Sophie suggests trapping the fertiliser compounds in **insoluble** pellets to be put on the soil. Explain why this idea will **not** help to provide the crops with fertiliser.

....

....

Q5 Suggest **three** pieces of advice on the use of fertilisers that could be given to farmers to help prevent **eutrophication**.

1. ....

2. ....

3. ....

Q6 **Ammonium nitrate** is often used as a fertiliser.

a) Name the acid and the base used to make ammonium nitrate.

acid: ....

base: ....

b) Name the element that ammonium nitrate is particularly good at providing to plants.

....

c) Explain why this element is important for plant growth.

....

Q7 Excessive use of fertilisers can cause pollution and eutrophication, but they are still widely used.

a) Given that the population of the world is increasing, explain why fertilisers are so widely used.

....

....

....

b) Ammonia is an important reactant in the production of fertilisers.
What effect do you think the rising population will have on the demand for ammonia?

....

....

Top Tips: Fertilisers are always given a lot of bad press but without them there'd be a lot less food to go round. The trick is not to use too much fertiliser — that'll stop those pesky environmental problems.

Preparing Fertilisers

Q1 Tamsin prepares **ammonium sulfate** in the lab using the apparatus shown in the diagram.

a) Name the two reactants Tamsin needs to use to make ammonium sulfate.

1. ....

2. ....

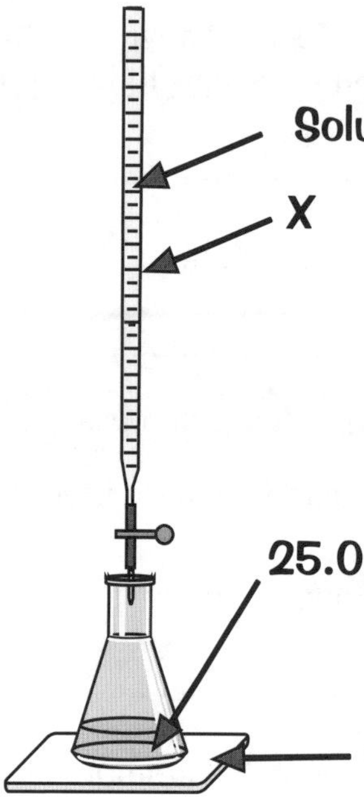

b) Suggest what piece of apparatus Tamsin used to accurately measure 25.0 cm^3 of solution B.

....

c) Name the piece of apparatus shown in the diagram that's labelled **X**.

....

d) What type of reaction is occurring?

....

e) Name an indicator Tamsin could use to decide when the reaction is finished.

....

f) Describe the method used to find the end point of the reaction

....

....

....

Tamsin finds that she needs 12.6 cm^3 of solution A for the reaction.
She repeats the experiment to obtain **pure** crystals of ammonium sulfate.

g) What important **difference** must she make to her experimental procedure to produce **pure** ammonium sulfate?

....

h) What volume of solution A must she add? ....

i) How can Tamsin get ammonium sulfate crystals from her ammonium sulfate solution?

....

....

The Haber Process

Q1 The Haber process is used to make **ammonia**.

a) Write a balanced symbol equation for the reaction that takes place in the Haber process.

.... + ... $\rightleftharpoons$ ....

b) Explain what the symbol $\rightleftharpoons$ tells you about this reaction.

....

Q2 The **industrial conditions** for the Haber process are carefully chosen.

a) What conditions are used? Tick one box.

☐ 1000 atmospheres, 450 °C	☐ 200 atmospheres, 1000 °C	☐ 450 atmospheres, 200 °C	☐ 200 atmospheres, 450 °C

b) Explain why the pressure used is chosen.

....

....

Q3 In the Haber process, the reaction is affected by the temperature.

a) What effect will raising the temperature have on the **amount** of ammonia formed?

....

b) Explain why a high temperature is still used industrially.

....

c) What happens to the leftover nitrogen and hydrogen? ....

Q4 The Haber process uses an **iron catalyst**.

a) What effect does this have on the % yield? ....

b) Iron catalysts are cheap. What effect does using one have on the **cost** of producing the ammonia? Explain your answer.

....

....

Top Tips: Changing the conditions in a reversible reaction to get more product sounds great, but don't forget that those conditions might make the reaction too slow to be profitable.

Minimising the Cost of Production

Q1 Use the following words to complete the blanks.

yield sufficient optimum rate recycled lowest

.... conditions are chosen to give the .... production cost per kg of product. This may mean that the conditions used do not have the highest .... of reaction or the highest percentage .... of product. However, both the rate and the yield must be high enough to give a .... daily yield of product. A low percentage yield is acceptable if the starting materials can be .... and reacted again.

Q2 Explain how the following affect the **production costs** of making a new substance.

a) Catalysts ....

....

b) Recycling raw materials ....

....

c) Automation ....

....

d) High temperatures ....

....

e) Very high pressure ....

....

Q3 A pharmaceutical company tests two production processes for producing a new drug. Rupert records both the total **production cost** and the total **yield** for each process over a one-week period.

a) Calculate the cost per g of drug for each process.

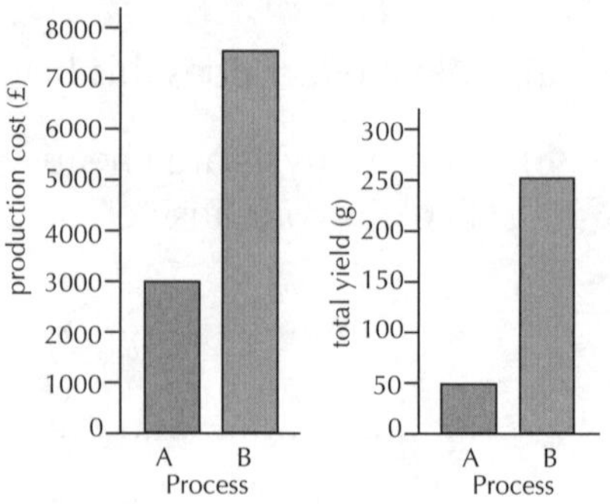

....

....

....

....

production cost (£)
8000
7000
6000
5000
4000
3000
2000
1000
0
A B
Process

total yield (g)
300
250
200
150
100
50
0
A B
Process

b) Suggest why the company decides to use process B, even though it has a higher production cost.

....

Salt

Q1 Indicate whether the following statements about obtaining salt are **true** or **false**.

		True	False
a)	In the UK most salt is obtained by evaporation in flat open tanks.	☐	☐
b)	There are massive deposits of rock salt in Cheshire.	☐	☐
c)	Salt can be mined by pumping hot water underground.	☐	☐
d)	Some holes left by mining salt must be filled in, or they could cause subsidence.	☐	☐

Q2 **Circle** the correct answer for each of the questions below.

a) One of the products of the electrolysis of brine is chlorine. You can test for it by:

Using a glowing splint — chlorine will relight it.

Using damp litmus paper — chlorine will bleach it.

Using universal indicator — chlorine will turn it purple.

b) Two of the products of electrolysis are reacted together to make household bleach. They are:

Chlorine and hydrogen.

Chlorine and sodium hydroxide.

Hydrogen and sodium hydroxide.

Q3 The diagram shows the **industrial set-up** used to electrolyse concentrated brine.

a) Identify the substances labelled A, B, C and D on the diagram. Choose from the options in the box below.

Na	O_2	Cl_2	H_2
brine	NaOH	H_2O	

A .... B ....

C .... D ....

b) Write **balanced** half-equations for the reactions that occur during the electrolysis of this salt solution.

Make sure the charges balance.

Anode: ....

Cathode: ....

c) i) State the electrode where oxidation take place. ....

ii) State the electrode where reduction take place. ....

d) Why are inert electrodes used?

....

Mixed Questions — Module C2

Q1 **Limestone** is a sedimentary rock.

a) Describe the main steps in the formation of sedimentary rocks.

....

....

....

b) Complete the following equation to show the **thermal decomposition** of limestone.

$CaCO_3 \rightarrow$ .... + ...

c) Limestone can be processed to form useful building materials. Complete the flow diagram.

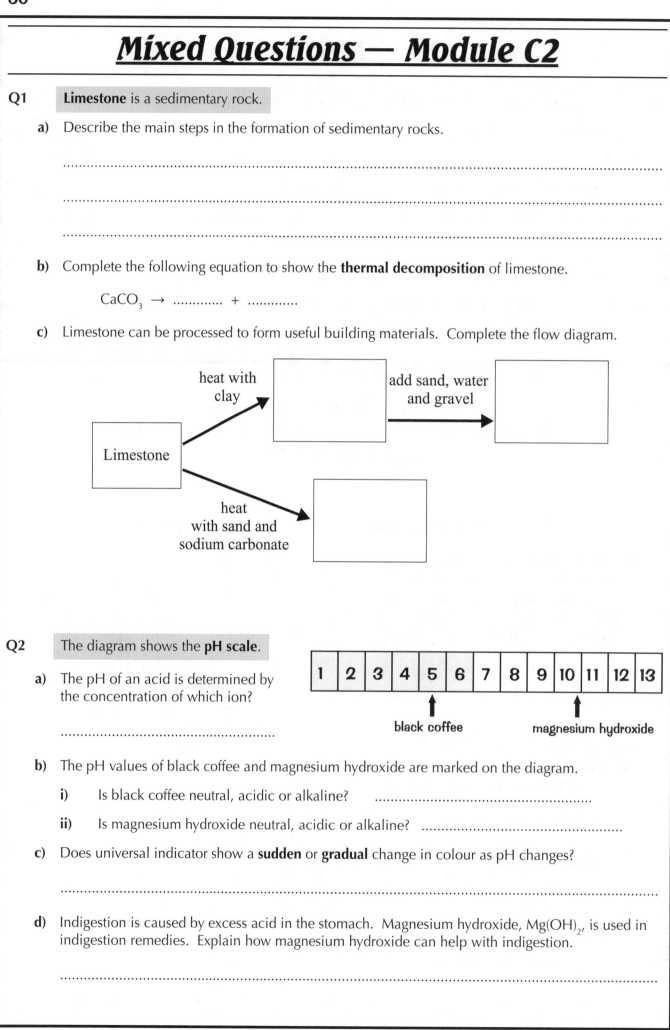

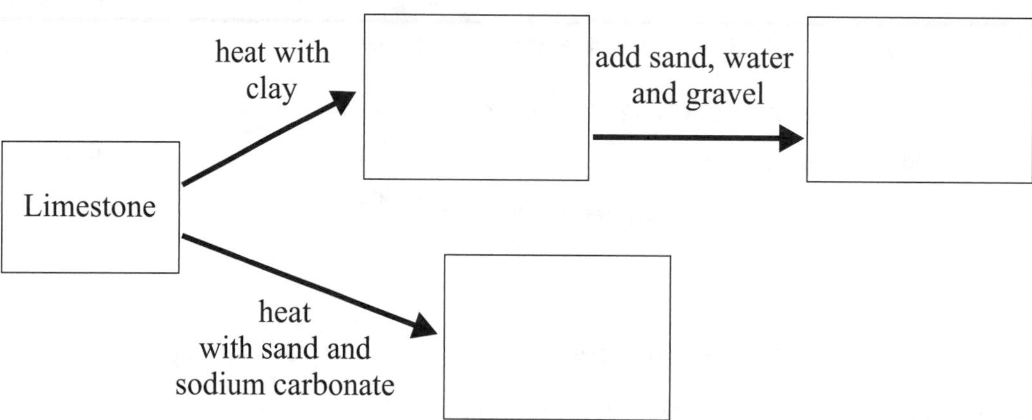

Q2 The diagram shows the **pH scale**.

1	2	3	4	5	6	7	8	9	10	11	12	13

black coffee (pH 5) — magnesium hydroxide (pH 10)

a) The pH of an acid is determined by the concentration of which ion?

....

b) The pH values of black coffee and magnesium hydroxide are marked on the diagram.

i) Is black coffee neutral, acidic or alkaline? ....

ii) Is magnesium hydroxide neutral, acidic or alkaline? ....

c) Does universal indicator show a **sudden** or **gradual** change in colour as pH changes?

....

d) Indigestion is caused by excess acid in the stomach. Magnesium hydroxide, $Mg(OH)_2$, is used in indigestion remedies. Explain how magnesium hydroxide can help with indigestion.

....

Mixed Questions — Module C2

Q3 Copper is a metal with a variety of uses.

a) Copper is dug out of the ground as an **ore**. Explain what an **ore** is.

....

b) Copper is used in **alloys**. Circle the alloys below which contain copper.

bronze amalgam brass steel solder nitinol

c) The diagram below shows how copper is purified. Label the **anode** and the **cathode**.

d) What makes copper atoms go into solution as ions?

....

....

e) Which electrode increases in size during the electrolysis?

....

f) What is purified copper used for in cars? Why is this?

....

g) Name another **metal** which is used in cars. What part of the car is it used for and why?

....

....

h) Suggest two pros of **recycling** the copper and other metals used in cars.

....

....

Q4 A **subduction zone** occurs where an oceanic plate and a continental plate collide.

a) What happens to the plates at a subduction zone?

....

....

b) Explain how volcanoes are formed near to a subduction zone.

....

....

c) Is the type of rock formed from volcanoes metamorphic, sedimentary or igneous?

....

Mixed Questions — Module C2

Q5 Chlorine, hydrogen and sodium hydroxide are produced by **electrolysing brine**.

a) Place each of the uses listed below into the correct box to show whether it is a use of chlorine, hydrogen or sodium hydroxide. Some uses may belong in more than one box.

PVC **soap** **solvents** **margarine** **disinfecting water** **bleach** **ammonia**

CHLORINE	HYDROGEN	SODIUM HYDROXIDE

b) Chlorine and sodium hydroxide are made by the **chlor-alkali industry**.
Apart from making useful products, give a reason why the chlor-alkali industry is so important.

....

c) Give the four ions that are present in brine.

1 .... 2 .... 3 .... 4 ....

d) **i)** What is produced at the anode during the electrolysis of brine? ....

ii) What is produced at the cathode during the electrolysis of brine? ....

Q6 The **Haber process** is used to produce ammonia.

a) Give **four factors** on which the cost of producing ammonia depends.

....

....

b) The temperature and pressure conditions for the Haber process could be described as '**a compromise**'. With reference to these conditions explain what the 'compromise' is.

....

....

....

c) Ammonia is used to produce ammonium nitrate fertiliser.
Explain how excess fertiliser on fields can kill fish in local rivers.

....

....

....

Energy Transfer in Reactions

Q1 Use the words to **complete** the passage below. Each word can be used more than once.

endothermic **exothermic** **energy** **heat** **an increase** **a decrease**

All chemical reactions involve changes in ....

In .... reactions, ... energy is given out to the surroundings. A thermometer will show .... in temperature.

In .... reactions, ... energy is taken in from the surroundings. A thermometer will show .... in temperature.

Q2 Fiz investigated the **temperature change** during a reaction. She added 25 cm^3 of sodium hydroxide solution to 25 cm^3 of hydrochloric acid. She recorded the temperature of the reaction mixture at **15 second intervals** for **two minutes**.

Fiz plotted her results on the graph shown.

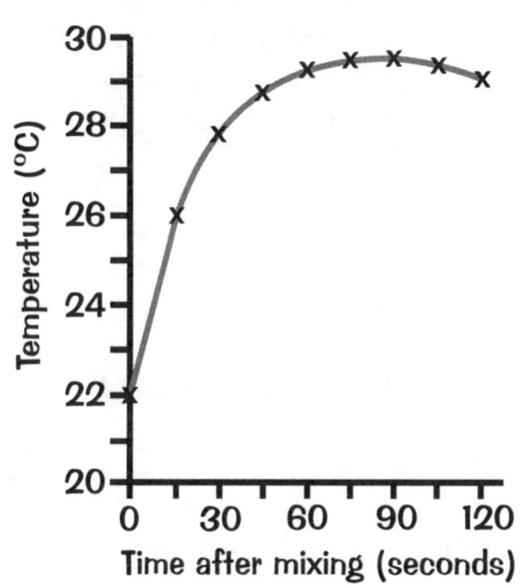

a) What was the increase in temperature due to the reaction?

....

b) Circle any of the words below that correctly describe the reaction in this experiment.

decomposition **combustion**

endothermic **respiration** **exothermic**

Q3 **Circle** the correct words to complete each of the sentences below.

a) An example of an endothermic reaction is **thermal decomposition** / **combustion**.

b) Bond breaking is an **exothermic** / **endothermic** process.

c) Bond making is an **exothermic** / **endothermic** process.

Q4 As the reaction shown below takes place, the temperature of the reaction mixture **increases**.

A B + C → A C + B

a) Is this reaction exothermic or endothermic? ....

b) Which bond is stronger, A–B or A–C? Explain your answer.

....

....

Measuring the Energy Content of Fuels

Q1 Write down the formulas for calculating:

a) the energy transferred to water during a calorimetric experiment.

....

b) the energy output of a fuel per gram.

....

Q2 Ross wants to compare the **energy content** of two fuels, petrol and a petrol alternative, fuel X.

a) In the box on the right, draw a labelled diagram showing the apparatus Ross could use to compare the energy content of the two fuels in a simple calorimetric experiment.

b) Name **two variables** that Ross has to **control** to ensure a fair test when using this method.

....

c) Suggest how Ross could make sure that his results were **reliable**.

....

d) He finds that **0.7 g** of petrol raises the temperature of **50 g** of water by **30.5 °C**.

i) Calculate the energy gained by the water.

....

ii) Use your answer to **i)** to calculate the energy released per gram of petrol. Give your answer in units of **kJ/g**.

....

e) Burning **0.8 g** of fuel X raises the temperature of **50 g** of water by **27 °C**. Calculate the energy released per gram of fuel X.

....

....

f) Using this evidence only, decide whether petrol or fuel X would make the better fuel. Explain your choice.

....

Chemical Reaction Rates

Q1 Match these common chemical reactions to the **speed** at which they happen.

a firework exploding | SLOW (hours or longer) | iron rusting

hair being dyed | MODERATE SPEED (minutes) | a match burning

an apple rotting | FAST (seconds or shorter) | oil paint drying

Q2 Tick the boxes to show whether the following statements are **true** or **false**.

		True	False
a)	When particles collide they always react.	☐	☐
b)	The greater the frequency of collisions, the greater the rate of reaction.	☐	☐
c)	Collision theory helps us to explain rates of reaction.	☐	☐

Q3 Two particles are moving around in a reaction mixture. Name **two** factors that determine whether or not they will **react** with each other.

1. ....

2. ....

Q4 Joe measured the **rate** of a reaction. He added 1 g of **calcium carbonate powder** to 100 cm^3 of **dilute hydrochloric acid**. The equation for the reaction that took place is shown below.

$$CaCO_3 + 2HCl \rightarrow CaCl_2 + CO_2 + H_2O$$

Think about the states of the products.

a) Joe measured the reaction rate by recording how the mass of the mixture changed over time. After two minutes there was still some powder left at the bottom of the flask, but the mass of the reaction mixture had stopped changing.

i) State which reactant is the limiting reactant ....

ii) Explain your answer to part **i)**. ....

....

b) Joe is going to repeat the experiment. This time he plans to add half as much of the limiting reactant. What will happen to the amount of calcium chloride produced? Explain your answer.

....

....

....

Collision Theory

Q1 Draw lines to match up the changes with their effects on the particles.

increasing the temperature

decreasing the concentration

adding a catalyst

increasing the surface area

provides a surface for particles to stick to and lowers activation energy

makes the particles move faster, so they collide more often

means more of a solid reactant will be exposed to particles of the other reactant

means fewer particles of reactants are present, so fewer collisions occur

Q2 Reactions involving gases are affected by the **pressure**.

a) In the boxes on the right, draw two diagrams, one showing particles of two different gases at low pressure, the other showing the gases at high pressure.

low pressure | high pressure

b) i) If you increase the pressure of reacting gases, will the rate of reaction **increase** or **decrease**? ....

ii) Explain your answer.

....

....

Q3 Here are five statements about **surface area** and rates of reaction. Tick the appropriate box to show whether each is **true** or **false**.

		True	False
a)	Breaking a solid into smaller pieces decreases its surface area.	☐	☐
b)	A larger surface area will mean a faster rate of reaction.	☐	☐
c)	A larger surface area decreases the number of useful collisions.	☐	☐
d)	Powdered marble has a larger surface area than the same mass of marble chips.	☐	☐
e)	A powdered solid reactant produces more product overall than an equal mass of reactant in large lumps does.	☐	☐

Q4 Circle the correct words to complete the sentences below.

a) In order for a reaction to occur, the particles must **remain still / collide**.

b) If you make a solution more concentrated it means there are **more / less** reactant particles in the same volume.

c) This means that the reactant particles are **more / less** likely to collide with each other.

d) So, increasing the concentration **increases / decreases** the rate of reaction.

Collision Theory

Q5 Choose words from the list below to complete the paragraph.

successful	slowing down	slower	speeding up
faster	energy	decreases	increases

When a reacting mixture is heated, the particles move ....

This .... the frequency of collisions. It also gives the particles

more .... so more collisions are ....

All this leads to the reaction ....

Q6 The sign on the right is displayed on the doors of a factory that makes **custard powder**. Other than hygiene, explain why these rules are important.

DANGER
NO SMOKING, MATCHES OR OPEN LIGHTS

....

....

....

Q7 Karen's chemistry teacher gives her a sample of a mystery chemical. He tells her that the chemical is a catalyst for this reaction: $\mathbf{2H_2O_2 \rightarrow O_2 + 2H_2O}$

a) Explain what a catalyst is.

....

....

b) How much of the catalyst does Karen need to add in order to increase the reaction rate? Circle the best answer below.

A very small amount.　　　　A very large amount.

c) Karen tries adding a bit of the mystery chemical to a different reaction. Is it likely that the mystery chemical will speed up this reaction too? Explain your answer.

....

....

Top Tips: Collision theory is all about the probability of reactants bumping into each other. Anything that makes things bump more often will also increase the rate of the reaction.

Rate of Reaction Data

Q1 Sam conducted two experiments with equal masses of marble chips and equal volumes of hydrochloric acid (HCl). He used two **different concentrations** of acid and measured the **change in mass** of the reactants. Below is a graph of the results.

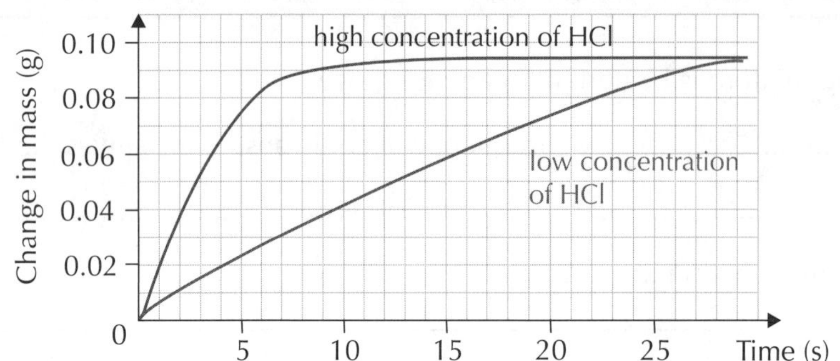

a) Calculate the average rate of reaction for the first five seconds for:

i) the experiment carried out with a high concentration of HCl.

....

ii) the experiment carried out with a low concentration of HCl.

....

b) Circle the letter(s) next to any valid conclusion(s) below that you might draw **from this graph**.

A **Increasing the concentration of the acid has no effect on the rate of reaction.**

B **Rate of reaction depends on the acid concentration.**

C **Rate of reaction depends on the mass of the marble chips.**

c) State what the **change in mass** will be for the experiment with the high concentration of HCl after **35 seconds**. ....

Q2 Eve investigated how **surface area** affects reaction rate. She added excess dilute hydrochloric acid to **large marble chips** and measured the loss of mass at regular intervals. She repeated the experiment using the same mass of **powdered marble**. Below is a graph of her results.

a) Which curve, A or B, was obtained when **large pieces** of marble were used? ....

b) On the graph opposite, draw:

i) the curve you would expect from the **same mass** of **medium** sized marble pieces. Label it C.

ii) the curve you would expect from **half** the mass of medium sized marble pieces. Label it D.

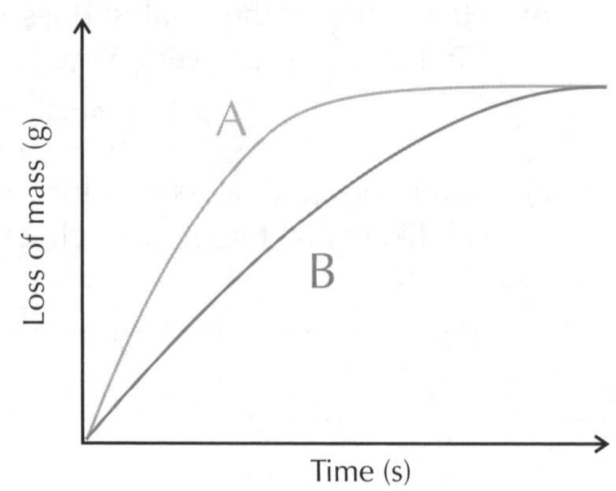

c) Is there enough information given above for you to be sure whether this was a **fair test** or not? Explain your answer.

....

....

Rate of Reaction Data

Q3 Pete measured how much **carbon dioxide** was given off during the reaction between 5 g of **marble chips** (calcium carbonate) and 100 cm³ of **hydrochloric acid**. His data is shown below.

	REACTION 1	REACTION 2
Time (s)	Volume of CO_2 produced (cm^3)	Volume of CO_2 produced (cm^3)
10	14	24
20	25	42
30	36	57
40	46	69
50	54	77
60	62	80
70	70	80
80	76	80
90	80	80
100	80	80

a) On the grid below, plot a graph of **volume of carbon dioxide** (vertical axis) against **time** (horizontal axis) for **reaction 1**. Label it.

b) On the same axes, plot a similar graph for **reaction 2**. Label it.

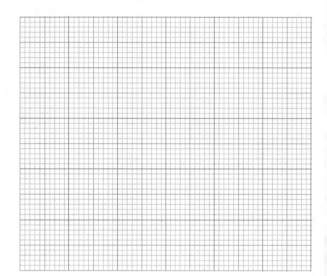

c) State which reaction is faster. Explain how you know this.

....

d) Suggest **three** things Pete might have done differently for **reaction 2** to cause the change in **rate**.

1. ....

2. ....

3. ....

e) On your graph label where:
i) reaction 2 **finished**.
ii) reaction 2 had its **fastest rate**.

f) Calculate the rate of reaction for both reaction 1 and reaction 2 for the first 20 s.

....

....

g) Does this back up your answer to part **c**)? ....

h) What volume of carbon dioxide had been produced in **reaction 1** after **25 seconds**? ....

Read the value off the graph you have drawn.

Top Tips: So, that's it in a nutshell — the faster a reaction goes, the steeper its graph will be, and when the reaction stops, the graph levels out. It's as easy as falling off a chemistry-based log... Ouch...

Reacting Masses

Q1 What are the **relative atomic masses (A_r)** of the following:

a) Magnesium .... **d)** Hydrogen .... **g)** K ....

b) Neon .... **e)** C .... **h)** Ca ....

c) Oxygen .... **f)** Cu .... **i)** Cl ....

Q2 Calculate the **relative formula masses (M_r)** of the following:

a) Water, H_2O ....

b) Nitric acid, HNO_3 ....

c) Ammonium nitrate, NH_4NO_3 ....

d) Calcium nitrate, $Ca(NO_3)_2$ ....

Q3 The balanced symbol equation below shows a reaction between **potassium** and **water**.

$$2K + 2H_2O \rightarrow 2KOH + H_2$$

a) Use relative formula masses to show that **mass is conserved** during this reaction

....

....

....

b) Explain why the **products** of a chemical reaction have **the same mass** as the **reactants**.

....

....

....

Q4 Tim heats 3.175 g of **copper** with **sulfur** to form **copper sulfide**.

Calculate how much copper sulfide will be produced using the masses of copper shown in the table below. All the copper reacts with all the sulfur to form copper sulfide.

Copper sulfide is the only product formed in this reaction.

Mass of copper / g	Mass of sulfur / g	Mass of copper sulfide / g
63.5	32	
31.75		
3.175		

Calculating Masses in Reactions

Q1 Anna burns **10 g** of **magnesium** in air to produce **magnesium oxide** (MgO).

a) Write out the **balanced equation** for this reaction.

....

b) Calculate the mass of **magnesium oxide** that's produced.

....

....

....

Q2 What mass of **sodium** (**Na**) is needed to make **2 g** of **sodium oxide** (**Na_2O**)?

The equation for this reaction is $4Na + O_2 \rightarrow 2Na_2O$

....

....

....

Q3 **Aluminium** and **iron oxide** (Fe_2O_3) react together to produce **aluminium oxide** (Al_2O_3) and **iron**.

a) Write out the **balanced equation** for this reaction.

....

b) What **mass** of iron is produced from **20 g** of iron oxide?

....

....

....

Q4 **Propane** (C_3H_8) burns in **oxygen** (O_2) to give **carbon dioxide** (CO_2) and **water** (H_2O).

How many grams of propane would you need to burn to make **1.65 g** of **carbon dioxide**?

....

....

....

....

Atom Economy

Q1 **Copper oxide** can be reduced to copper by burning it with carbon.

copper ore + carbon → copper + carbon dioxide

$2CuO + C \rightarrow 2Cu + CO_2$

Relative formula masses: **CuO = 79.5, C = 12, Cu = 63.5, CO_2 = 44**

a) What is the useful product in this reaction? ....

b) Calculate the **atom economy** of the reaction. ....

....

c) Calculate what percentage of the starting materials are wasted.

....

Q2 Explain why industrial reactions with a **high atom economy** are better than reactions with a **low atom economy**.

....

....

....

Q3 The two reactions shown below are both used industrially to make **ethanol** (CH_3CH_2OH).

Reaction 1: $C_2H_4 + H_2O \rightarrow CH_3CH_2OH$ **Reaction 2:** $C_6H_{12}O_6 \rightarrow 2CH_3CH_2OH + 2CO_2$

a) State which of these two reactions has a 100% atom economy. ....

b) Give a reason for your answer to part **a)**.

....

....

Q4 **Titanium** can be reduced from titanium chloride ($TiCl_4$) using magnesium or sodium.

a) Work out the atom economy for each reaction.

With magnesium: $TiCl_4 + 2Mg \rightarrow Ti + 2MgCl_2$ ....

....

With sodium: $TiCl_4 + 4Na \rightarrow Ti + 4NaCl$ ....

....

b) Which one has the better atom economy? ....

Percentage Yield

Q1 James wanted to produce **silver chloride** (AgCl). He added a carefully measured mass of silver nitrate to an excess of dilute hydrochloric acid. An **insoluble white salt** formed.

a) Write down the formula for calculating the **percentage yield** of a reaction.

b) James calculated that he should get 2.7 g of silver chloride, but he only got 1.2 g. What was the **percentage yield**?

....

....

Q2 The **percentage yield** of industrial processes needs to be as high as possible.

a) Explain why chemical reactions that are used in industry need to have high percentage yields.

....

....

b) Explain why **evaporation** can affect the percentage yield of a reaction.

....

....

....

Q3 Aaliya and Natasha mixed together barium chloride ($BaCl_2$) and sodium sulfate (Na_2SO_4) in a beaker. An **insoluble** substance formed. They **filtered** the solution to obtain the solid substance, and then transferred the solid to a clean piece of **filter paper** and left it to dry.

a) Aaliya calculated that they should produce a yield of **15 g** of barium sulfate. However, after completing the experiment they found they had only obtained **6 g**.

Calculate the **percentage yield** for this reaction.

....

....

b) Suggest two reasons why their actual yield was lower than their predicted yield.

1. ....

2. ....

Chemical Production

Q1 Suggest whether **continuous** or **batch** production would be used to make the following chemicals.

a) Perfumes ....

b) Sulfuric acid ....

c) Ammonia ....

d) Paints ....

Q2 Widely used chemicals are often produced by **continuous production**.

a) Circle the correct words to complete the following sentences.

Continuous production is often used for the **small-scale / large-scale** production of chemicals.
It's **highly automated / labour-intensive**, which means that there are low labour costs.
Continuous production means that the quality of products is very **consistent / inconsistent.**

b) State two **disadvantages** of continuous production.

1. ....

2. ....

Q3 **Batch production** is used to produce specialist chemicals.

a) Use these words to complete the blanks about batch production.

inflexible **high** **small** **quality** **large** **versatile** **low**

Batch production is often used for manufacturing .... quantities of specialist chemicals. The advantages of batch production are that the plant is .... (allowing for many different products to be made), and that the costs of plant equipment are .... Disadvantages of batch production include the .... labour costs and the difficulties in maintaining the same .... of product from batch to batch.

b) Why are **pharmaceutical drugs** usually manufactured using batch production?

....

....

Chemical Production

Q4 Compounds used in pharmaceutical drugs are often extracted from **plants**.

a) Describe the following steps in the extraction process.

A B C

Step A ....

Step B ....

Step C ....

b) Give **two** reasons why companies spend money and time on trials for new drugs.

1. ....

2. ....

c) **i)** The melting temperature of a drug is 82 °C. State which of the following samples is a pure sample of the drug and give a reason for your answer.

Sample 1 = 80 ° C **Sample 2 = 82 °C** **Sample 3 = 86 °C**

....

....

ii) Step C is carried out on a pure sample of the drug.
Describe and explain what the results of Step C would look like.

....

....

Q5 Tony decides his pharmaceutical company should develop and manufacture a new drug.

a) Give two reasons why the **research** and **development** of new pharmaceutical drugs is expensive.

1. ....

2. ....

b) Give two reasons why the **manufacturing** process of pharmaceutical drugs is expensive.

1. ....

2. ....

Allotropes of Carbon

Q1 **Diamond**, **graphite**, and **fullerenes** are all **allotropes** of carbon.

a) Explain the meaning of the term '**allotropes**'.

....

b) The structures of **three** allotropes of carbon are shown below.
Write the **name** of each allotrope under the diagrams.

i)

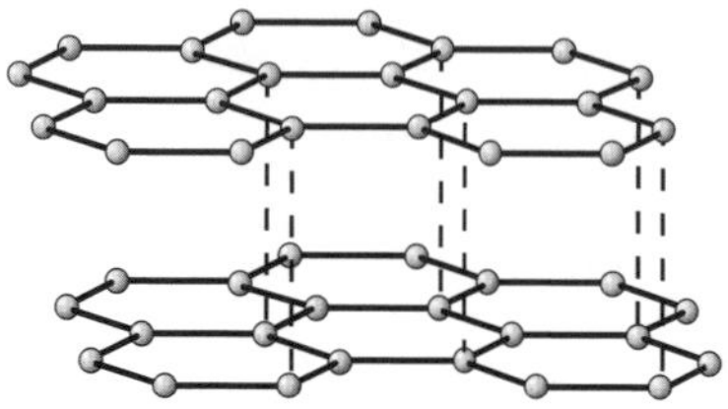

....

ii)

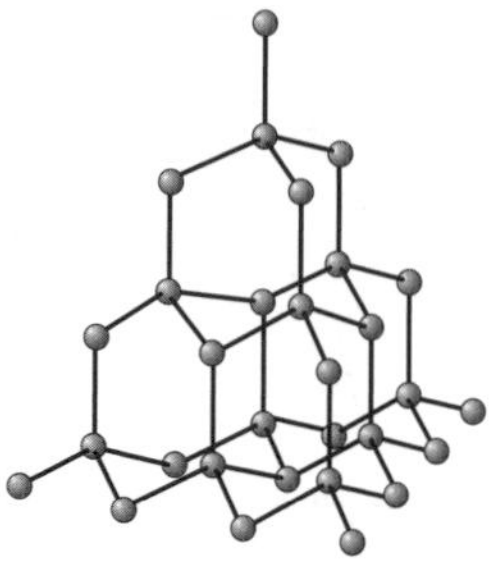

....

iii)

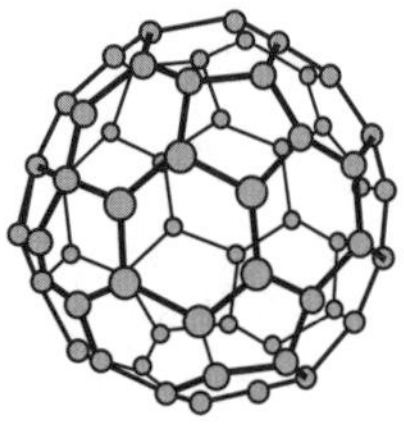

....

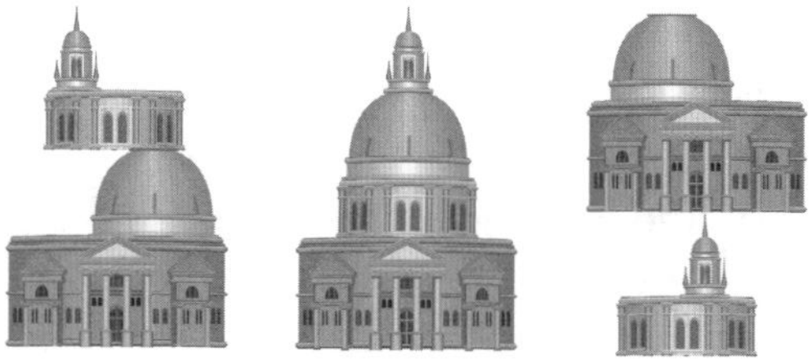

c) Both diamond and graphite are giant molecular structures.
Give **two** properties of a giant molecular structure.

1. ....

2. ....

Q2 **Fullerenes** are an allotrope of carbon.

a) Fullerenes can be used to 'cage' other molecules. Give a potential use for this technology.

....

b) What are **nanotubes**?

....

c) Briefly explain why nanotubes are used to make **industrial catalysts**.

....

....

Top Tips: There's more than one allotrope of carbon you've got to know about and you need to know what they are, what their uses are and why they're suitable for these uses. Hmmm, thrilling.

Allotropes of Carbon

Q3 **Graphite** is an allotrope of carbon.

a) Fill in the gaps in the passage using words from the list below.

four	red	tools	lubricant	tightly	three	high
low	black	loosely	slide	delocalised		

Graphite is made of layers of carbon that are held .... together. It is .... in colour. Within the layers, each carbon atom forms .... covalent bonds. These strong covalent bonds give graphite a .... melting point. Between the layers there is only a weak attraction. This enables the layers to .... easily over each other, which makes it useful as a ....

b) Explain why graphite is **able** to conduct electricity.

....

....

c) Give two reasons why graphite is used in pencil leads.

1. ....

2. ....

Q4 **Diamond** is another allotrope of carbon.

a) Circle the correct words to complete the sentences below about diamond.

Diamond has a **simple molecular** / **giant covalent** structure. Each carbon atom in diamond forms **three** / **four** covalent bonds with neighbouring atoms.
Because it has lots of strong covalent bonds diamond has a **low** / **high** melting point and is very **soft** / **hard**, which makes it ideal for use in **lubricants** / **cutting tools**.

b) Why is diamond **unable** to conduct electricity?

....

c) Name two properties of diamond that make it useful for **jewellery**.

1. ....

2. ....

Mixed Questions — Module C3

Q1 Lee is investigating how changing the **concentration** of acid that he uses affects the rate of a reaction.

a) The diagram on the right shows the acid particles present in a solution of **dilute acid**.

In the box, complete the diagram showing the **same volume** of **concentrated acid**.

b) Explain how increasing the **concentration** of the acid will affect the reaction rate.

....

....

....

c) Using the axes on the right:

i) Sketch the reaction rate curve you would expect to see when Lee uses a **high** concentration of acid.

ii) Sketch the reaction rate curve you would expect to see when Lee uses a **low** concentration of acid.

(Assume that the acid is not the limiting reactant.)

d) Name two things Lee will need to keep constant in order to make it a **fair experiment**.

1. ....

2. ....

Q2 **30 g** of a fuel, X, is burnt and used to heat **100 g** of water. The temperature of the water before heating was **20 °C**, and after heating it was **42 °C**.

The specific heat capacity of water = 4.2 J/g °C

a) Calculate the energy transferred **per gram** of this fuel.

....

....

....

b) What name is given to a reaction like this one that gives out energy? ....

c) Which quantity of energy is the larger in this reaction? Underline the correct answer.

The energy required to break the old bonds. **The energy released in forming the new bonds.**

Mixed Questions — Module C3

Q3 The graph on the right shows the results of three **rate of reaction experiments** using **magnesium** and dilute **hydrochloric acid**.

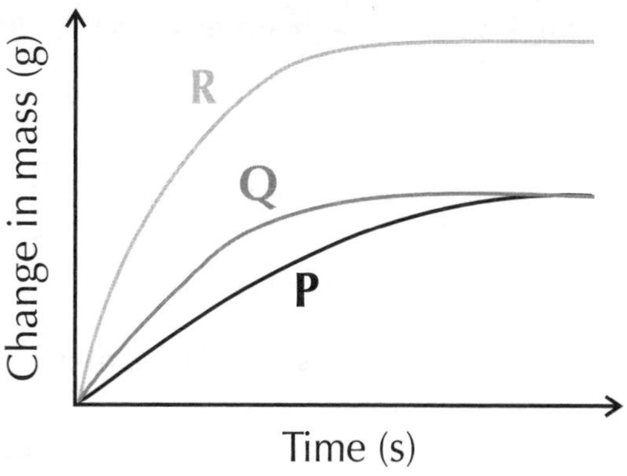

Change in mass (g)
R
Q
P
Time (s)

a) Which reaction was **faster**, P or Q?

....

b) Which reaction started off with the **largest** amount of limiting reactant, P, Q or R?

....

c) Mark with an X on the graph the point at which reaction R finished.

Q4 **Calcium carbonate** will thermally decompose to give **calcium oxide** and **carbon dioxide**.

a) Complete the **balanced symbol equation** for this reaction, shown below.

.... (s) $\longrightarrow$ CaO (s) + ... (g)

b) Calculate the relative formula masses of:

i) Calcium carbonate ....

ii) Calcium oxide ....

iii) Carbon dioxide ....

c) This reaction is used industrially to produce **calcium oxide**.

i) Calculate the mass of calcium carbonate you would need to make **15 g** of calcium oxide.

....

....

....

ii) Calculate the **atom economy** of the reaction.

....

....

d) The thermal decomposition of calcium carbonate is **endothermic**. What will happen to the temperature of the surroundings as the reaction happens? Explain your answer.

....

....

Mixed Questions — Module C3

Q5 The **Haber Process** is used to manufacture **ammonia** (NH_3). The reactants are **hydrogen gas** (H_2) and **nitrogen gas** (N_2).

a) Write a word equation for the reaction that creates ammonia.

....

b) Write a **balanced symbol equation** for the same reaction.

....

c) Calculate how much ammonia you would expect to produce from 12 g of nitrogen gas.

Nitrogen has an A_r of 14.
Hydrogen has an A_r of 1.

....

....

....

....

d) The actual yield from 12 g of nitrogen gas is about 1.82 g of ammonia. Calculate the percentage yield of the reaction.

The yield of this reaction is low because it is **reversible**. To reduce waste, any unused reactants are **recycled**.

....

....

....

e) A solid iron catalyst is added to the reaction mixture. Circle the correct words to complete the following sentences about the catalyst.

i) Adding an iron catalyst **increases / doesn't affect** the rate of the reaction between nitrogen and hydrogen.

ii) Adding an iron catalyst **increases / doesn't affect** the yield of ammonia.

f) Ammonia is usually produced using **continuous production**.

i) Give one advantage of producing ammonia in this way.

....

ii) Give one disadvantage of producing ammonia in this way.

....

The History of the Atom

Q1 The theory of **atomic structure** has changed a lot over the past two hundred years. Draw lines to place these landmark theories on the time line in the **correct order**.

beginning of the 19th century → present day

J J Thomson's plum pudding model.	Bohr's electron shell theory.	Dalton's solid spheres.	Rutherford's theory of the nuclear atom.

Q2 **Bohr's** theory was pretty close to our present day view of the atom.

a) Describe Bohr's model of the atom.

....

....

b) Bohr's model was different to previous theories. Why was his theory accepted by scientists?

....

Q3 J J Thomson developed the **plum pudding model** of the atom.

Remember to label the positive and negative parts.

a) Draw and label a diagram of this model in the box on the right.

b) Describe how J J Thompson's model of the atom differed from Dalton's model of the atom.

....

....

....

Q4 Geiger and Marsden conducted an experiment known as the '**gold foil experiment**'.

a) Briefly describe how this experiment was conducted.

....

b) Describe what they observed.

....

c) Explain why these results were significant.

....

....

Atoms

Q1 **Complete** the following sentences.

a) Neutral atoms have a charge of ....

b) The nucleus is made up of .... and ....

c) Atoms have a mass of about .... grams.

d) A neutral atom has the same number of .... and ....

e) Atoms have a radius of about .... metres.

Q2 **Complete** this table.

Particle	Mass	Charge
Proton	1	
	1	0
Electron		–1

Q3 Elements have a **mass number** and an **atomic number**.

a) What does the **mass number** of an element tell you?

....

b) What does the **atomic number** of an element tell you?

....

c) Fill in this table using a periodic table.

Element	Symbol	Mass Number	Number of Protons	Number of Electrons	Number of Neutrons
Sodium	Na		11		
		16	8	8	8
Neon			10	10	10
	Ca			20	20

Q4 In the periodic table **carbon** (C) is written like this: $^{12}_{6}C$

a) Circle the mass number.

b) Underline the atomic number.

c) How many protons does carbon have? ....

d) How many electrons does this carbon have? ....

e) How many neutrons does this carbon have? ....

Elements and Isotopes

Q1 Select from these **elements** to answer the following questions.

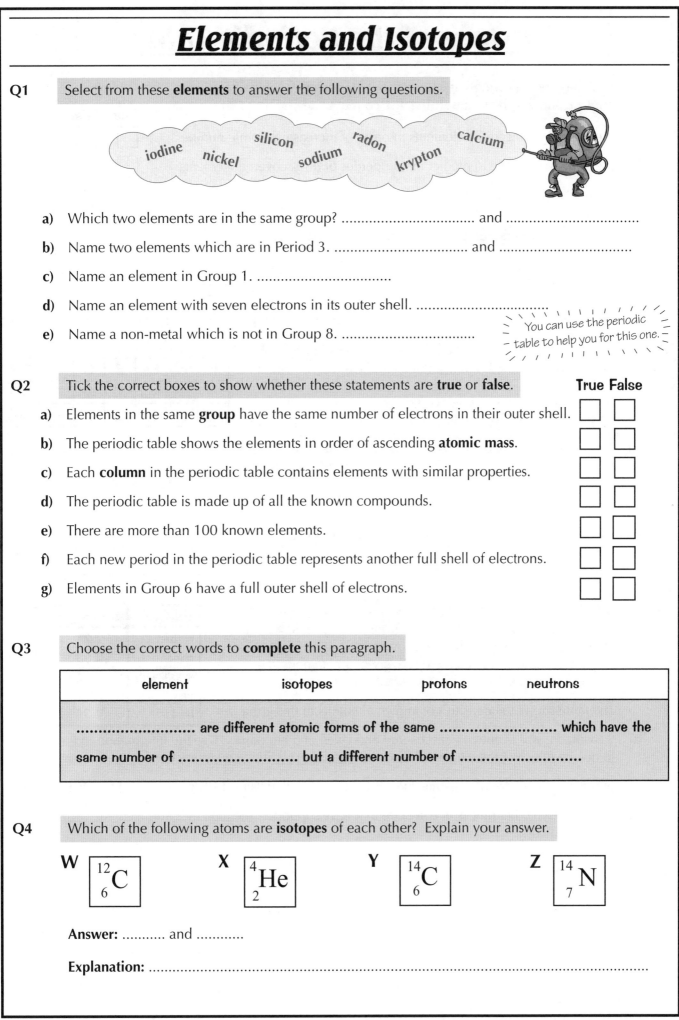

iodine nickel silicon sodium radon krypton calcium

a) Which two elements are in the same group? .... and ....

b) Name two elements which are in Period 3. .... and ....

c) Name an element in Group 1. ....

d) Name an element with seven electrons in its outer shell. ....

e) Name a non-metal which is not in Group 8. ....

You can use the periodic table to help you for this one.

Q2 Tick the correct boxes to show whether these statements are **true** or **false**.

	True	False
a) Elements in the same **group** have the same number of electrons in their outer shell.	☐	☐
b) The periodic table shows the elements in order of ascending **atomic mass**.	☐	☐
c) Each **column** in the periodic table contains elements with similar properties.	☐	☐
d) The periodic table is made up of all the known compounds.	☐	☐
e) There are more than 100 known elements.	☐	☐
f) Each new period in the periodic table represents another full shell of electrons.	☐	☐
g) Elements in Group 6 have a full outer shell of electrons.	☐	☐

Q3 Choose the correct words to **complete** this paragraph.

element	isotopes	protons	neutrons

.... are different atomic forms of the same .... which have the same number of .... but a different number of ....

Q4 Which of the following atoms are **isotopes** of each other? Explain your answer.

W $^{12}_{6}C$ **X** $^{4}_{2}He$ **Y** $^{14}_{6}C$ **Z** $^{14}_{7}N$

Answer: .... and ....

Explanation: ....

History of the Periodic Table

Q1 Which of the following statements about **Mendeleev's** Table of Elements are **true** and which are **false**? Tick the correct boxes.

		True	False
a)	Mendeleev arranged the elements in order of increasing atomic number.	☐	☐
b)	Mendeleev was able to predict the properties of undiscovered elements.	☐	☐
c)	Elements with similar properties appeared in the same rows.	☐	☐

Q2 Describe how **Döbereiner** chose elements for his **triads**.

....

....

Q3 When **Newlands** arranged the known elements in order of **atomic mass** in 1864, the first three rows were as shown.

	1					2
H	Li	Be	B	C	N	O
F	Na	Mg	Al	Si	P	S
Cl	K	Ca	Cr	Ti	Mn	Fe

a) In which of the two highlighted groups do the elements have similar properties? ....

b) This arrangement of elements was known as 'Newlands' Octaves'. Why did Newlands arrange the elements in rows of seven?

....

c) Give one criticism of Newlands' arrangement of the elements.

....

Q4 Mendeleev left **gaps** in his Table of Elements to keep elements with similar properties in the same groups. He predicted that elements would eventually be discovered to fill the gaps. For example, he predicted the discovery of an element that would fill a gap in his Group 4 and called it '**ekasilicon**'.

The table shows the **densities** of known elements in this group.

Element	Density g/cm³
carbon	2.27
silicon	2.33
'ekasilicon'	
tin	7.29
lead	11.34

a) 'Ekasilicon' was eventually discovered and given another name. Use the information in the table to decide which of the elements below is 'ekasilicon'. Circle your choice.

palladium, 12.02 g/cm³ germanium, 5.32 g/cm³ beryllium, 1.85 g/cm³ copper, 8.93 g/cm³

b) Describe two other pieces of evidence that have supported Mendeleev's arrangement of the elements.

1. ....

....

2. ....

....

Electron Shells

Q1 a) Tick the boxes to show whether the statements are **true** or **false**.

	True	False
i) Electrons occupy shells.	☐	☐
ii) The highest energy levels are always filled first.	☐	☐
iii) The first shell can hold 8 electrons.	☐	☐
iv) Noble gases have a full outer shell of electrons.	☐	☐
v) The third shell can hold 8 electrons.	☐	☐

b) Write out corrected versions of the **false** statements.

....

....

....

Q2 Identify **two** things that are wrong with this diagram.

1. ....

....

2. ....

....

Q3 Write out the **electronic configuration** for each of the following elements.

Use the periodic table to help you here.

a) Beryllium ....

b) Oxygen ....

c) Silicon ....

d) Calcium ....

e) Aluminium ....

f) Argon ....

Q4 Write down the **period** and **group** for elements with the following electronic structures.

a) **2, 8, 4** period .... group ....

b) **2, 2** period .... group ....

c) **2, 3** period .... group ....

d) **2, 8, 8** period .... group ....

Electron Shells

Q5 **Chlorine** has an atomic number of 17.

a) What is chlorine's electron configuration? ....

b) Draw the electrons on the shells in the diagram.

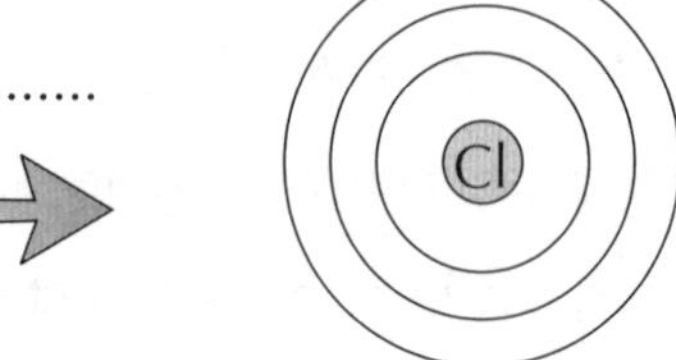

Q6 Draw the **full electronic structures** of these elements. (The first three have been done for you.)

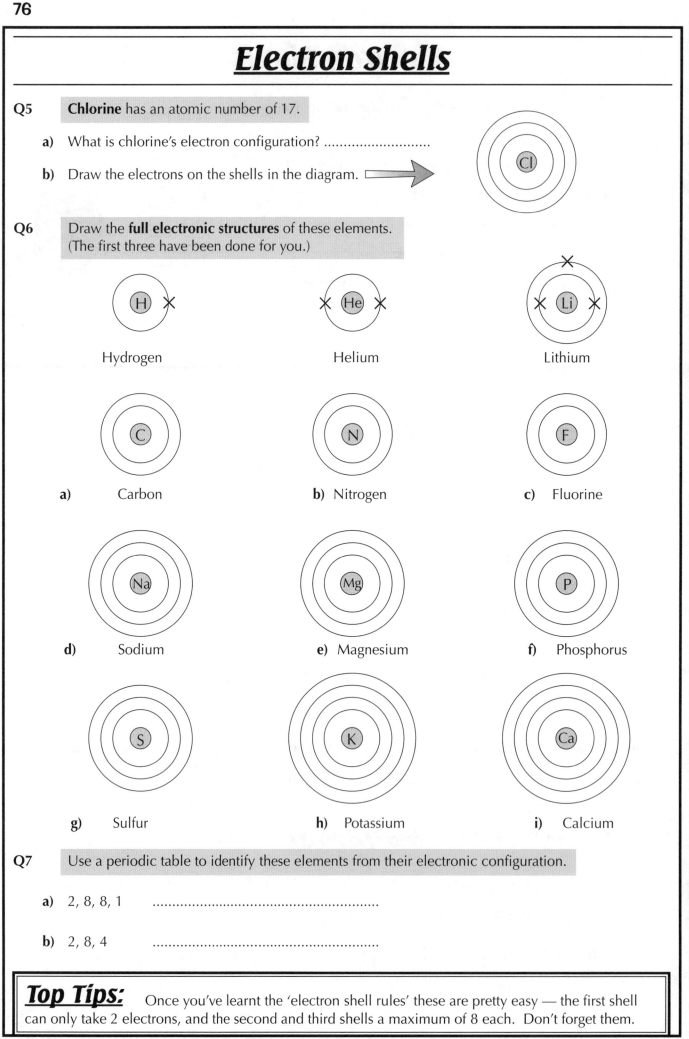

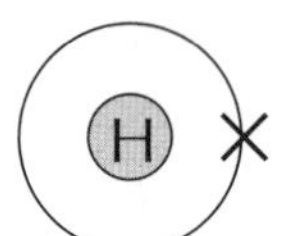

Hydrogen

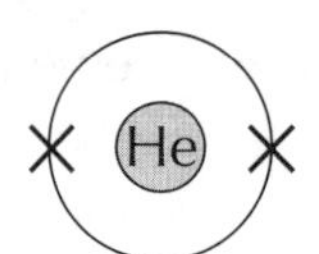

Helium

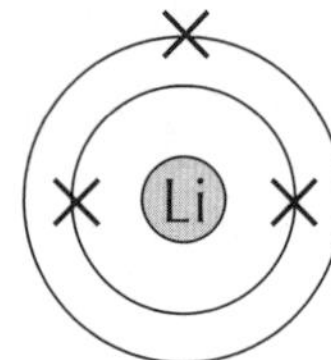

Lithium

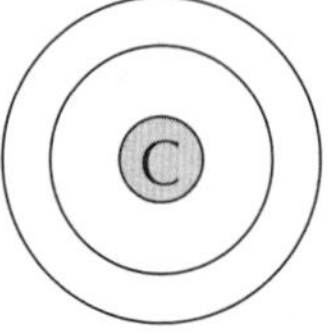

a) Carbon

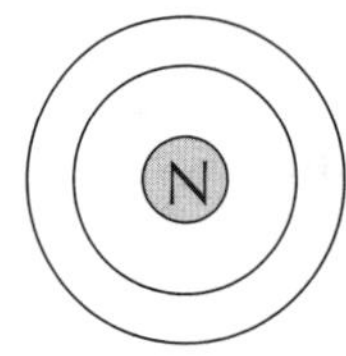

b) Nitrogen

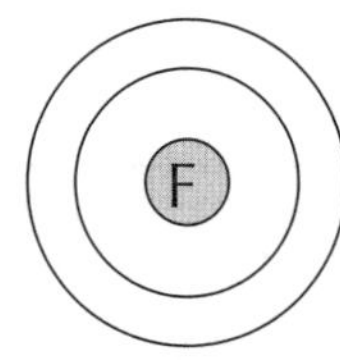

c) Fluorine

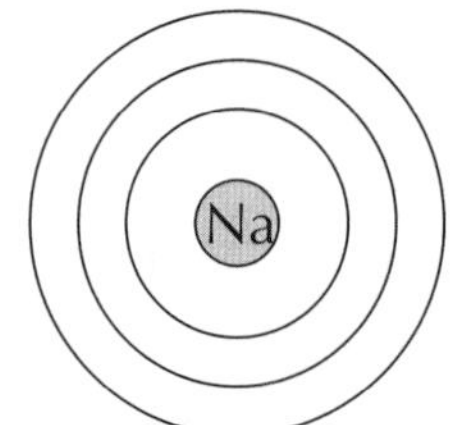

d) Sodium

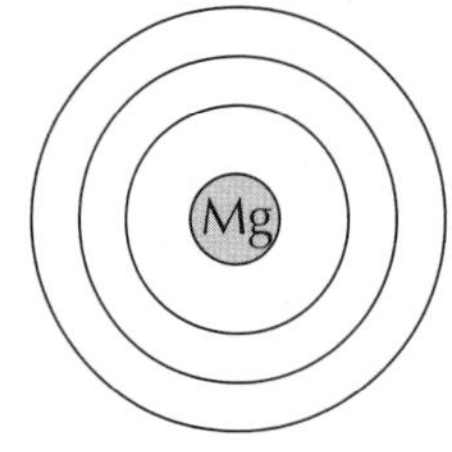

e) Magnesium

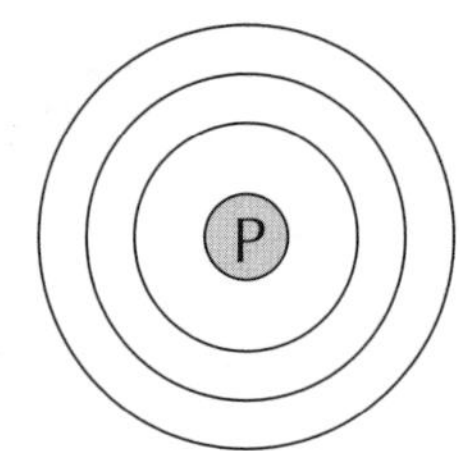

f) Phosphorus

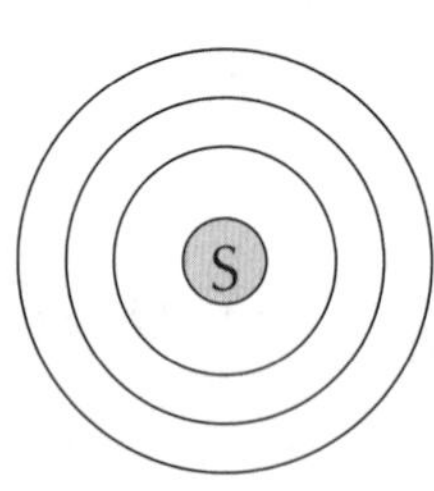

g) Sulfur

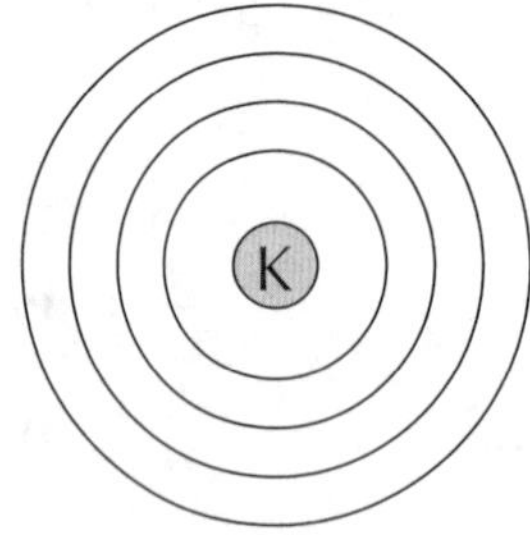

h) Potassium

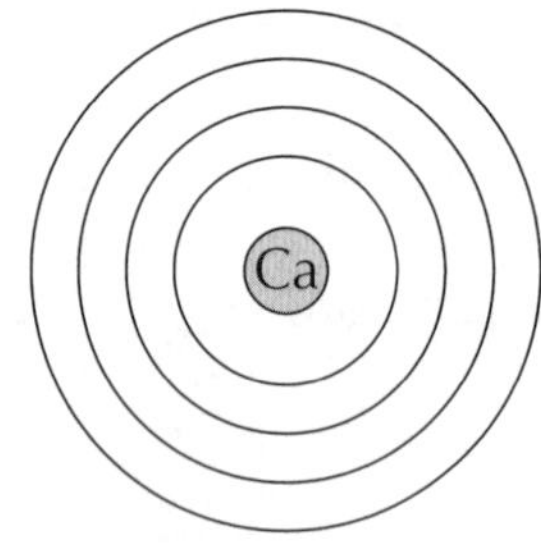

i) Calcium

Q7 Use a periodic table to identify these elements from their electronic configuration.

a) 2, 8, 8, 1 ....

b) 2, 8, 4 ....

Top Tips: Once you've learnt the 'electron shell rules' these are pretty easy — the first shell can only take 2 electrons, and the second and third shells a maximum of 8 each. Don't forget them.

Ionic Bonding

Q1 Fill in the gaps in the sentences below by choosing the correct words from the box.

protons	charged particles	repelled by	
electrons	ions	attracted to	neutral particles

a) In ionic bonding atoms lose or gain .... to form ....

b) Ions are ....

c) Ions with opposite charges are strongly .... each other.

Q2 **Magnesium oxide** is formed from two ions.

a) What name is given to the structure of magnesium oxide?

....

b) Circle the correct words to explain why magnesium oxide has a high melting point.

> Magnesium oxide has very **strong** / **weak** attraction between the **negative** / **positive** magnesium ions and the **negative** / **positive** oxygen ions. This means that it takes a **small** / **large** amount of energy to overcome the attraction and melt the compound.

c) Sodium chloride is another ionic compound. Sodium forms 1^+ ions and chlorine forms 1^- ions.

i) Will sodium chloride have a higher or lower melting point than magnesium chloride? ....

ii) Explain your answer.

....

....

....

....

Q3 Mike conducts an experiment to find out if **sodium chloride** conducts electricity. He tests the compound when it's solid, when it's dissolved in water and when it's molten.

	Conducts electricity?
When solid	
When dissolved in water	
When molten	

a) Complete the table of results opposite.

b) Explain your answers to part a).

....

....

Ions and Ionic Compounds

Q1 Tick the correct boxes to show whether the following statements are **true** or **false**.

		True	False
a)	Ions of metals and non-metals attract one another to form ionic compounds.	☐	☐
b)	Metals form negatively charged ions.	☐	☐
c)	Ions with a 2+ charge have gained 2 electrons.	☐	☐
d)	Elements in Group 7 gain electrons when they react.	☐	☐
e)	Atoms form ions because they are more stable when they have full outer shells.	☐	☐
f)	Elements with a full outer shell are very reactive.	☐	☐
g)	The number of electrons lost or gained is equal to the charge on the ion.	☐	☐

Q2 Here are some elements and the ions they form:

Make sure the charges on the ions balance.

beryllium, Be^{2+} **potassium, K^{+}** **iodine, I^{-}** **sulfur, S^{2-}**

Write down the formulas of four compounds which can be made using these elements.

1. .... 2. ....

3. .... 4. ....

Q3 Draw '**dot and cross**' diagrams showing the formation of the following ionic compounds:

a) **sodium oxide (Na_2O)**

b) **magnesium chloride ($MgCl_2$)**

c) **magnesium oxide (MgO)**

Top Tips: The big thing to remember about ionic compounds is... the charges always **balance**. The oppositely charged ions then strongly attract each other to create an ionic compound. Lovely.

Covalent Bonding

Q1 Indicate whether each statement is **true** or **false**.

		True	False
a)	Covalent bonding involves sharing electron pairs.	☐	☐
b)	Metals form covalent bonds.	☐	☐
c)	Some atoms can make both ionic and covalent bonds.	☐	☐
d)	Hydrogen can form two covalent bonds.	☐	☐
e)	Carbon can form four covalent bonds.	☐	☐

"Oi, give me that electron big nose!"

Q2 Carbon dioxide and water are both covalently bonded molecules. Complete these sentences by circling the correct word from each pair.

a) Substances that contain covalent bonds usually have **giant** / **simple** molecular structures.

b) Atoms within covalent molecules are held together by **strong** / **weak** covalent bonds.

c) Intermolecular forces between water molecules are **strong** / **weak**.
This results in **high** / **low** melting and boiling points.

d) Carbon dioxide has no free electrons so it **does** / **doesn't** conduct electricity.

Q3 Complete the following diagrams by adding **electrons**. Only the **outer shells** are shown.

Use • and x to show the electrons from the different elements.

a) Hydrogen (H_2)

H H

b) Chlorine (Cl_2)

Cl Cl

c) Carbon dioxide (CO_2)

O C O

d) Water (H_2O)

O H H

e) Methane (CH_4)

H H C H H

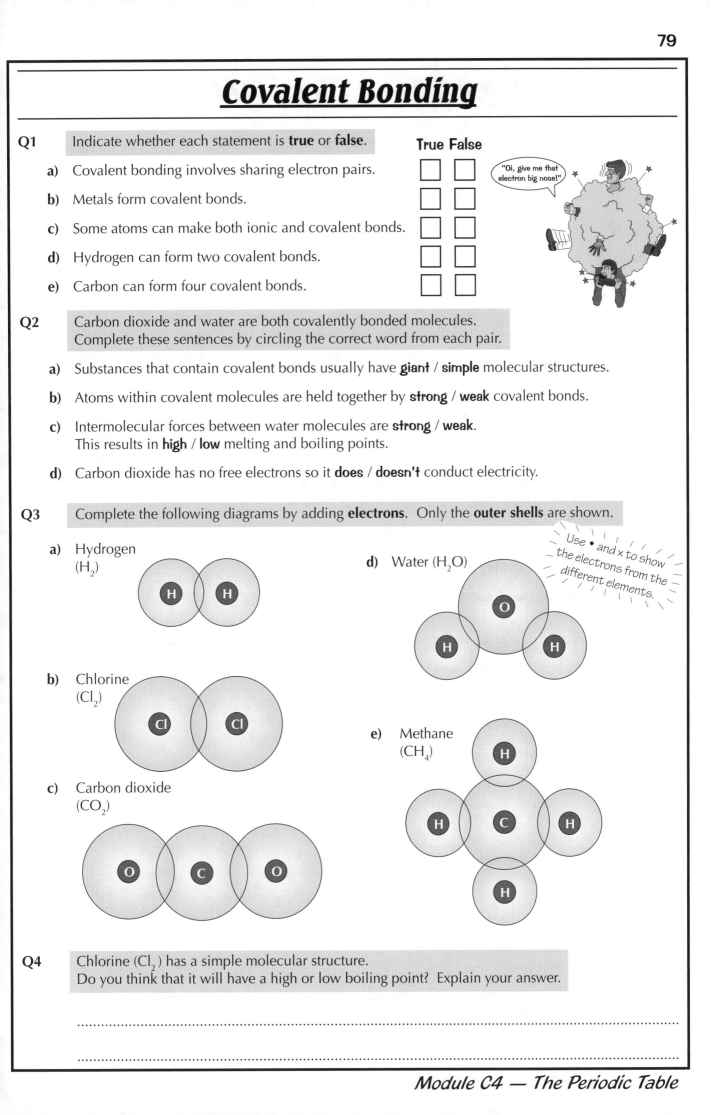

Q4 Chlorine (Cl_2) has a simple molecular structure.
Do you think that it will have a high or low boiling point? Explain your answer.

....

....

Group 1 — Alkali Metals

Q1 Indicate whether the statements below are **true** or **false**.

		True	False
a)	Alkali metals readily gain electrons to form 1^+ ions.	☐	☐
b)	Alkali metals form covalent compounds by sharing electrons.	☐	☐
c)	Alkali metals are stored in oil to stop them reacting with oxygen and water in the air.	☐	☐
d)	Alkali metal atoms all have a single electron in their outer shell.	☐	☐
e)	Alkali metals are hard.	☐	☐
f)	Alkali metals have similar properties because they all react to lose one electron.	☐	☐

Q2 The table shows the **melting points** of some Group 1 metals.

Element	Melting point (°C)
Li	181
Na	98
K	63
Rb	39
Cs	?

a) What is unusual about the **melting points** of the alkali metals compared to other metals?

....

b) Would you expect the melting point of **caesium** to be higher or lower than **rubidium**? Explain your answer.

....

c) Complete the following sentence:

As you move down Group 1, the reactivity of the atoms ....

Q3 Archibald put a piece of **lithium** into a beaker of water.

Archibald

"squeaky pop!"

a) Explain why the lithium floated on top of the water.

....

b) After the reaction had finished, Archibald tested the pH of the water. Would it be **alkaline** or **acidic**? Explain your answer.

....

....

c) Write a **balanced symbol equation** for the reaction.

....

d) i) Write a word equation for the reaction between rubidium and water.

....

ii) Would you expect the reaction between rubidium and water to be **more** or **less** vigorous than the reaction between lithium and water? Explain your answer.

....

Group 1 — Alkali Metals

Q4 Alkali metal compounds emit characteristic **colours** when put in a flame.

a) Selina has three powdered samples of alkali metal compounds. Describe an experiment she could carry out to help her identify the alkali metal present.

....

....

....

....

b) Which **alkali metal** is present in:

i) an alkali metal nitrate (found in gunpowder) that produces a lilac flame? ....

ii) a street lamp that emits an orange light? ....

iii) fireworks that produce red flames? ....

Q5 Sodium and potassium are **alkali metals**.

a) Draw the electronic arrangements of a **sodium atom** and a **potassium atom** in the space provided.

b) **i)** Write a balanced symbol equation to show the formation of a sodium ion from a sodium atom.

....

ii) Is this process oxidation or reduction? Explain your answer.

....

c) Why do sodium and potassium have similar properties?

....

d) Why is potassium more reactive than sodium?

....

....

Top Tips: All the alkali metals have a single outer electron, which they're dead keen to get rid of so they have a nice full outer shell. As you move down the group the outer electron gets further away from the nucleus so it's lost more easily — this makes the elements more reactive as you go down the group.

Group 7 — Halogens

Q1 Draw lines to match each halogen to its **description**.

chlorine (Cl_2)	dense green gas
iodine (I_2)	orange liquid
bromine (Br_2)	dark grey solid

Hubba hubba

Q2 Tick the correct boxes to say whether these statements are **true** or **false**.

		True	False
a)	Chlorine gas is made up of molecules which each contain three chlorine atoms.	☐	☐
b)	The halogens become less reactive as you go down the group.	☐	☐
c)	Chlorine and bromine are poisonous.	☐	☐
d)	The halogens readily gain electrons to form 1^+ ions.	☐	☐

Q3 Chlorine and bromine are both **halogens**.

a) Draw the electron arrangements of a **chlorine atom** and a **chloride ion** in the space provided.

b) **i)** Write a balanced symbol equation to show the formation of chloride ions from a chlorine molecule.

....

ii) Is this process oxidation or reduction? Explain your answer.

....

c) Why do chlorine and bromine have similar properties?

....

d) Why is bromine less reactive than chlorine?

....

....

Group 7 — Halogens

Q4 **Sodium** was reacted with **bromine vapour** using the equipment shown. White crystals of a new solid were formed during the reaction.

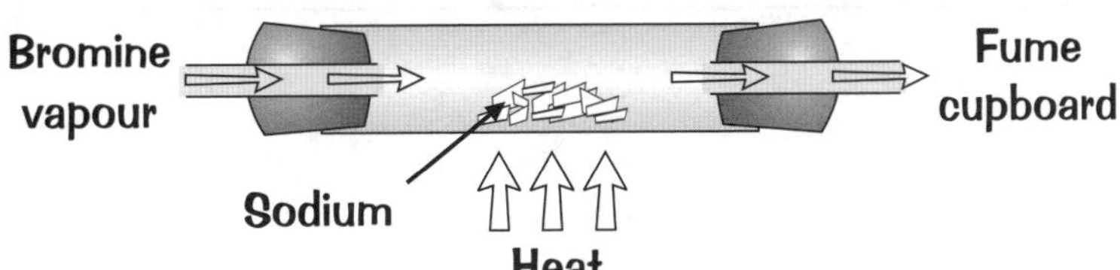

a) Name the white crystals.

....

b) Write a balanced symbol equation for the reaction.

....

c) Would you expect the above reaction to be faster or slower than a similar reaction between:

i) sodium and iodine vapour? Explain your answer.

....

ii) sodium and chlorine vapour? Explain your answer.

....

Q5 Equal volumes of **bromine solution** were added to two test tubes, each containing a different **potassium halide solution**. The results are shown in the table.

SOLUTION	RESULT
potassium chloride	no colour change
potassium iodide	colour change

a) Explain these results.

....

....

....

b) Write a **balanced symbol equation** for the reaction in the potassium iodide solution.

....

c) Would you expect a reaction between:

i) bromine solution and potassium astatide? ....

ii) bromine solution and potassium fluoride? ....

Metals

Q1 Draw a diagram in the space below to show the arrangement of the particles in a typical **metal**. Label the **ions** and the **free electrons**, and show any relevant charges.

An irrelevant charge.

Q2 The table shows the properties of **four elements** found in the periodic table.

ELEMENT	MELTING POINT (°C)	DENSITY (g/cm^3)	ELECTRICAL CONDUCTIVITY
A	1084	8.9	Excellent
B	-39	13.6	Very good
C	3500	3.51	Very poor
D	1536	7.87	Very good

a) Which three of the above elements are most likely to be **metals**?

....

b) Explain how you know the other element is **not** a metal.

....

....

Q3 Circle the phrase which best describes **metallic bonding**.

Strong attraction between delocalised electrons and close packed positive metal ions.

Strong attraction between bonding electrons and close packed positive metal ions.

Strong attraction between delocalised electrons and close packed negative metal ions.

Q4 Explain how **electricity** is conducted through metals.

....

....

Metals

Q5 Complete the following sentences by choosing from the words in the box.

Don't use any words more than once.

hammered	weak	low	high	strong	malleable	folded

a) Metals have a .... tensile strength.

b) Metals are .... and hard to break.

c) Metals can be .... into different shapes because they are ....

Q6 Explain why most metals have **high melting points**.

....

....

Q7 **Metals** are used for different things depending on their **properties**.

For each of the uses below, choose the most suitable metal from the list and state one property of the metal that makes it suitable for this purpose.

stainless steel   copper   aluminium   steel

a) Structures like bridges.

Metal ....

Property ....

b) Aeroplanes.

Metal ....

Property ....

c) Cutlery.

Metal ....

Property ....

d) Electrical wiring.

Metal ....

Property ....

Top Tips: Okay, so metals form weird bonds. How come the electrons can go wandering about like that? Well actually, that's just the kind of question you **don't** need to ask yourself right now. Don't stress about it, just learn the key phrases examiners like — '**sea of delocalised electrons**,' etc.

Superconductors and Transition Metals

Q1 Draw lines to match the transition metal to the process it catalyses.

iron	hydrogenation of alkenes
nickel	ammonia production

Q2 Complete the passage below by circling the correct word(s) from each pair.

> Most metals are in the transition block found **at the left / in the middle** of the periodic table. They are generally **good / poor** conductors of heat and electricity, have high **densities / volatility** and **low / high** melting points. Their compounds are **colourful / shiny** and, like the metals themselves, are often effective **fuels / catalysts**.

Q3 Under normal conditions **all** metals have **electrical resistance**.

a) Describe how electrical resistance causes energy to be wasted.

....

....

b) What is a superconductor? ....

c) Give three possible uses of superconducting wires.

1. ....

2. ....

3. ....

d) Explain a drawback of using today's superconductors.

....

....

Q4 'Colourful chemical gardens' can be made by sprinkling **transition metal salts** into **sodium silicate solution**. Transition metal silicate crystals grow upwards as shown.

a) Why do you think transition metal salts are used?

....

b) Suggest three colours that you would be likely to see in the garden if iron(II) sulfate, iron(III) chloride and copper(II) sulfate salts are used.

....

Thermal Decomposition and Precipitation

Q1 Draw lines to match the type of reaction with its description.

thermal decomposition

precipitation

when a substance breaks down into two or more simpler substances when heated

where two solutions react and an insoluble solid is formed

Q2 Neil heats some **green** copper carbonate, $CuCO_3$. He is left with a **black** solid.

a) How can Neil tell that a reaction has taken place?

....

b) What type of reaction has taken place? ....

c) Write a word equation for this reaction.

....

d) Describe how you could **test** for **carbon dioxide**.

....

....

Q3 Write **balanced symbol equations** for the thermal decomposition of the following substances.

a) zinc carbonate, $ZnCO_3$

....

b) iron(II) carbonate, $FeCO_3$

....

c) copper(II) carbonate, $CuCO_3$

....

d) manganese(II) carbonate, $MnCO_3$

....

Top Tips: Thermal decomposition — what a name. But it's not as difficult as it sounds. Take one reactant. Heat it up until it falls apart into two or more bits and there you go — one thermal decomposition reaction. Simple. The tricky bit is learning all those symbol equations...

Thermal Decomposition and Precipitation

Q4 Clear, blue **copper(II) sulfate solution** and clear, colourless **sodium hydroxide** solution were mixed. The liquid went cloudy and pale blue. After a while a **pale blue solid** was left at the bottom and the liquid was **clear** again.

a) What type of reaction has occurred? ....

b) Name the blue solid formed.

....

c) Write a balanced symbol equation for this reaction.

....

d) Write a symbol equation to show the formation of the pale blue solid.

....

Q5 Cilla adds a few drops of **NaOH** solution to solutions of different **metal compounds**.

a) Complete her table of results.

Compound	Metal Ion	Colour of Precipitate
copper(II) sulfate		blue
iron(II) sulfate		
iron(III) chloride	Fe^{3+}	
copper(II) chloride		

b) Write a balanced symbol equation for the reaction of copper(II) chloride with sodium hydroxide.

....

These reactions could also happen with lithium hydroxide (LiOH) or potassium hydroxide (KOH).

c) Complete the balanced ionic equation for the reaction of iron(II) ions with hydroxide ions.

Fe^{2+} + ... OH^- → ....

d) Write a balanced ionic equation for the reaction of **iron(III) ions** with hydroxide ions.

....

e) Explain how this type of reaction could be used to help identify unknown metal ions.

....

....

....

Water Purity

Q1 There are a variety of water resources in the UK.

a) Which one of the following water resources is a source of 'groundwater'? Circle your answer.

reservoirs aquifers rivers lakes

b) Name three important uses of water in **industrial processes**.

....

....

Q2 Explain why it is important to conserve water.

....

....

Q3 Water is **treated** before it reaches our homes.

a) Number the stages 1– 4 to show the correct order of the processes in a **water treatment** plant.

☐ Sedimentation ☐ Filtration through sand beds

☐ Chlorination ☐ Filtration through a wire mesh

b) Why are two filtration processes needed? ....

....

c) Name a chemical used in the sedimentation process. ....

d) Why are the purification processes unable to remove impurities such as ammonium nitrate?

....

e) Why is chlorination used in the purification process?

....

Q4 Helen's house has an **old plumbing system**. She's concerned about **pollutants** in the tap water.

a) What form of pollution in the tap water could be caused by the plumbing system?

....

b) Helen's water supply comes from a reservoir located in an area of intensive agriculture. Suggest **two** other forms of pollutant which could be present in the tap water.

....

Q5 Some countries get fresh water by **distilling** sea water. Give **one** disadvantage of using this method.

....

Testing Water Purity

Q1 **Sodium sulfate** reacts with **barium chloride** in a precipitation reaction.

a) What is a **precipitation reaction**?

....

b) Complete the word equation for this reaction.

sodium sulfate + barium chloride → barium .... + ...

c) Complete and balance the symbol equation for this reaction.

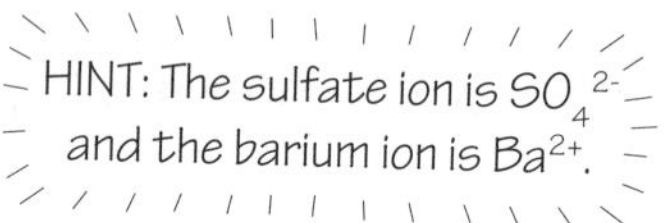

HINT: The sulfate ion is SO_4^{2-}
and the barium ion is Ba^{2+}.

Na_2SO_4 + ... → .... + ... NaCl

d) State the **colour** of the precipitate formed in this reaction.

....

Q2 Sam creates a flow chart as a key to help her identify **halide anions** present in a sample of water.

a) Finish the flow chart by completing the empty boxes.

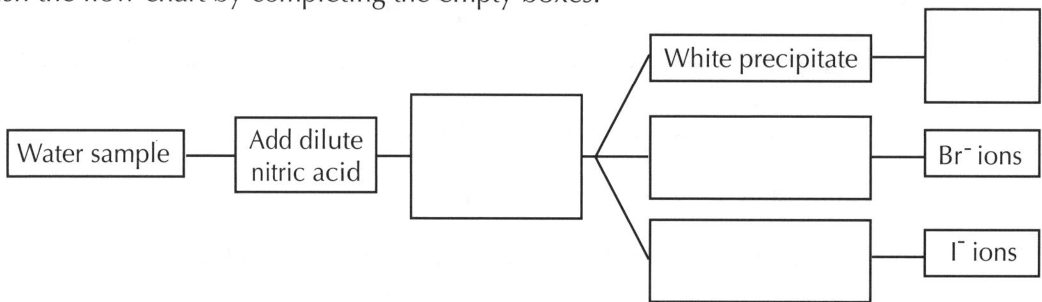

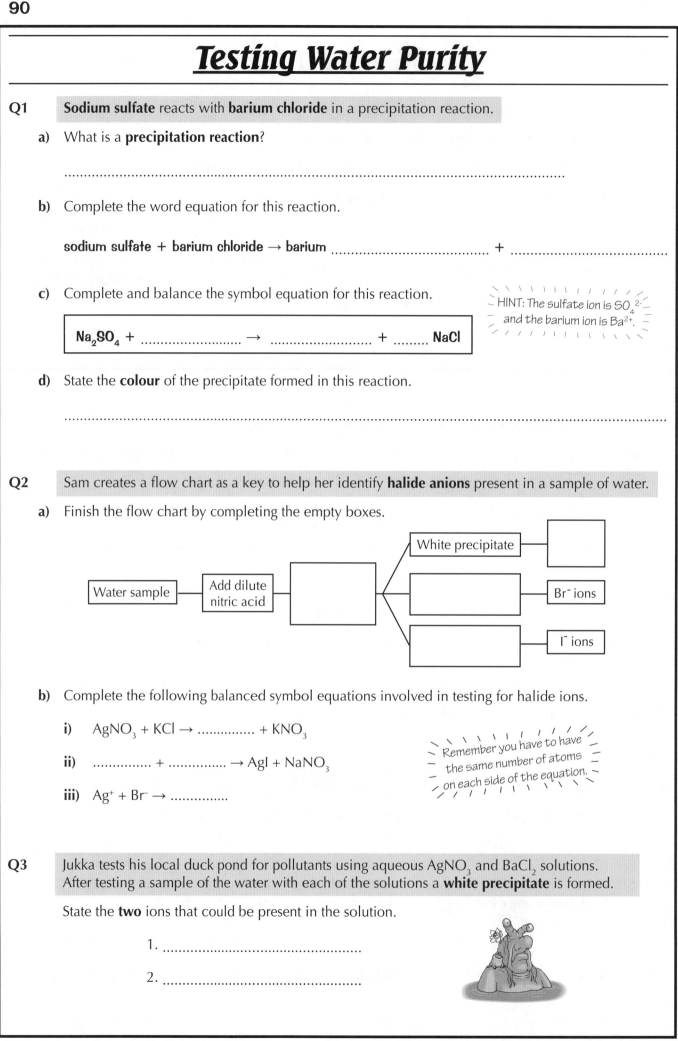

b) Complete the following balanced symbol equations involved in testing for halide ions.

i) $AgNO_3$ + KCl → .... + KNO_3

ii) .... + ... → AgI + $NaNO_3$

iii) Ag^+ + Br^- → ....

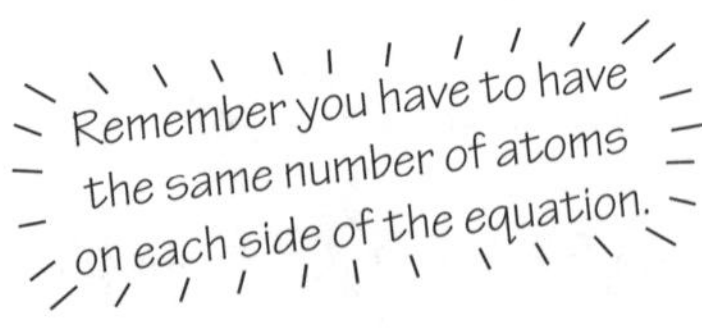

Remember you have to have
the same number of atoms
on each side of the equation.

Q3 Jukka tests his local duck pond for pollutants using aqueous $AgNO_3$ and $BaCl_2$ solutions. After testing a sample of the water with each of the solutions a **white precipitate** is formed.

State the **two** ions that could be present in the solution.

1. ....

2. ....

Mixed Questions — Module C4

Q1 Hydrogen atoms can exist as three **isotopes** — ^{1}H (hydrogen), ^{2}H (deuterium) and ^{3}H (tritium).

a) What is an isotope?

....

b) Complete the table.

isotope	number of protons	number of neutrons	number of electrons
^{1}H			
^{2}H			
^{3}H			

c) The atomic number is often left out of the isotope symbol.
For instance, it is acceptable to write ^{12}C for carbon-12 rather than $^{12}_{6}C$.

i) Define the term **atomic number**.

....

ii) Explain why the atomic number can be left out of the isotope symbol.

....

Q2 **Lithium** is a metallic element in **Group 1** of the periodic table.

a) Draw a diagram to show the electronic structure of a lithium atom.

Use the periodic table to help you.

b) Explain how lithium ions usually form.

....

c) **Fluorine** is in **Group 7** of the periodic table. Its electronic structure is shown below.

i) Draw a diagram to show the electronic structure of a fluoride **ion**.

ii) Give the chemical formula for the compound that forms between lithium and fluorine.

....

F

d) Complete this table.

Ion	Symbol	Mass Number	Number of Protons	Number of Electrons	Number of Neutrons
Lithium		7			
Fluorine			9		10

Mixed Questions — Module C4

Q3 The table below gives some data for five **elements**.

Element	Melting point (°C)	Density (g/cm^3)	Conducts electricity as solid?	Oxide of element	
				Colour (at 20 °C)	State (at 20 °C)
A	1455	8.9	Yes	Green	Solid
B	44	1.82	No	White	Solid
C	3550	3.51	No	Colourless	Gas
D	1535	7.86	Yes	Red	Solid
E	98	0.97	Yes	White	Solid

a) Two of the elements are transition elements. Identify them and explain your answers.

....

....

b) Give a use for one named transition element.

Transition element: .... Use: ....

Q4 Scientists are trying to develop superconductors that work at **higher temperatures** than is currently possible.

a) What temperature would it be ideal for superconductors to work at?

....

b) A scientist has developed a high temperature superconductor.
Explain why he/she would tell other scientists about the discovery.

....

....

Q5 Ronald has been given a mystery test tube containing solution X. He tests the solution using different chemicals. His results are shown below.

a) Identify solution X.

....

b) Explain your answer to part **a)**.

....

....

Test	Result
$AgNO_3$	Nothing happened
$BaCl_2$	A white precipitate was formed
NaOH	A pale blue precipitate was formed

....

Mixed Questions — Module C4

Q6 The diagram shows the apparatus used to react **chlorine** with **magnesium**.

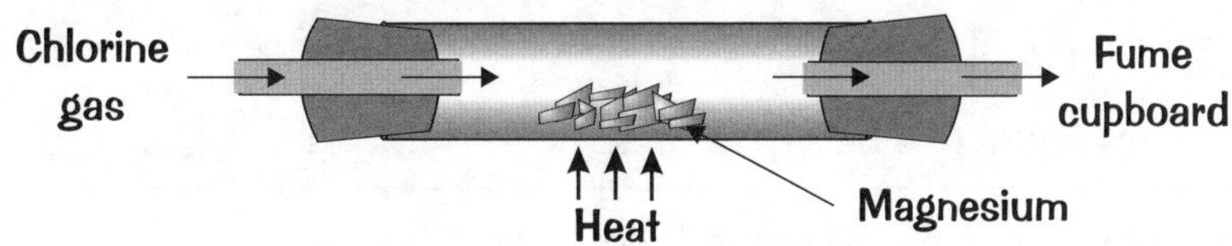

a) Why is it not possible to use the same apparatus to react iodine with magnesium?

....

b) Complete the chemical equation for the reaction: **Mg + Cl_2 →** ....

c) What type of bonding is present in the product? ....

d) Draw a dot and cross diagram to show the formation of magnesium chloride from magnesium and chlorine atoms.

e) Solid magnesium chloride does not conduct electricity. However, when magnesium chloride is dissolved in water or is molten it does conduct electricity. Explain these facts.

....

....

Q7 Metals are good **electrical conductors**. Explain why, using ideas about structure and bonding.

....

....

....

Q8 Iodine has a **simple molecular structure**.

a) What type of bonding binds the iodine atoms together in each molecule? ....

b) Explain why iodine has a low melting point.

....

....

c) Predict whether iodine is likely to be able to conduct electricity. Justify your prediction.

....

....

The Mole

Q1 a) **Complete** the following sentence.

> One mole of atoms or molecules of any substance will have a .... in grams equal to the .... for that substance.

b) What is the molar mass of each of the following?

Use a periodic table to help you. There's one at the front of this book.

i) C_2H_5OH ....

ii) $Cu(OH)_2$ ....

c) What is the mass of each of the following?

i) 2 moles of nitric acid, HNO_3. ....

ii) 0.5 moles of calcium carbonate, $CaCO_3$. ....

iii) 5.4 moles of magnesium hydroxide, $Mg(OH)_2$. ....

Q2 What is the **relative atomic mass** of an element?

....

....

Q3 a) Write down the formula for calculating the **number of moles in a given mass**.

....

b) How many **moles** are there in each of the following?

i) 54 g of aluminium, Al.

....

ii) 112 g of sulfur dioxide, SO_2.

....

iii) 198.75 g of copper oxide, CuO.

....

Q4 Calculate the **mass** of each of the following.

a) Magnesium in 0.75 moles of magnesium oxide, MgO.

....

b) Chlorine in 0.025 moles of lead chloride, $PbCl_2$.

....

Reacting Masses and Empirical Formulas

Q1 Use **atomic masses** to calculate the percentage by mass of the following elements in their compounds.

a) Cu in $CuSO_4$

....

b) C in C_5H_{10}

....

c) O in H_2O

....

Q2 Calculate the percentage by mass of an element using the following **experimental data**.

a) There is 5.48 g of H in 21.92 g of CH_4.

....

b) There is 13.44 g of C in 49.28 g of CO_2.

....

c) There is 57.6 g of S in 176.4 g of H_2SO_4.

....

d) There is 64.35 g of K in 166.65 g of KNO_3.

....

Q3 The equation below shows lead nitrate reacting with sodium chloride to form lead chloride and sodium nitrate.

$$Pb(NO_3)_2 + 2NaCl \rightarrow PbCl_2 + 2NaNO_3$$

Calculate the mass of lead chloride ($PbCl_2$) that is produced when 40.95 g of sodium chloride (NaCl) is used in the reaction.

....

....

....

Top Tips: When you're doing these types of questions remember to use your periodic table to find the all the atomic masses of the elements. Otherwise you might end up with the wrong numbers and that'll make all your calculations all higgledy piggledy, which is never a nice thing.

Reacting Masses and Empirical Formulas

Q4 The reaction between calcium carbonate and hydrochloric acid is shown below.

$$CaCO_3 + 2HCl \rightarrow CaCl_2 + CO_2 + H_2O$$

Calculate the mass of calcium carbonate ($CaCO_3$) that is required to produce 83.25 g of calcium chloride ($CaCl_2$).

....

....

....

Q5 Give the **empirical formula** for each of the following compounds.

a) $C_2H_4O_2$ .... **b)** C_4H_8 .... **c)** P_4O_{10} ....

Q6 Calculate the **empirical formula** of the compound formed when:

a) 20 g of calcium combines with 8 g of oxygen.

....

....

b) 5.4 g of aluminium combines with 9.6 g of sulfur.

....

....

Q7 An **oxide** of **sulfur** contains **60% oxygen**.

a) What is the percentage of sulfur in the oxide?

....

b) Calculate the empirical formula of the oxide.

....

....

Q8 A **carbonate** was found to contain **28.6% magnesium**, **14.3% carbon** and **57.1% oxygen**. Work out the **empirical formula** of the compound.

....

....

....

Concentration

Q1 a) Circle the correct word below to complete the following sentence.

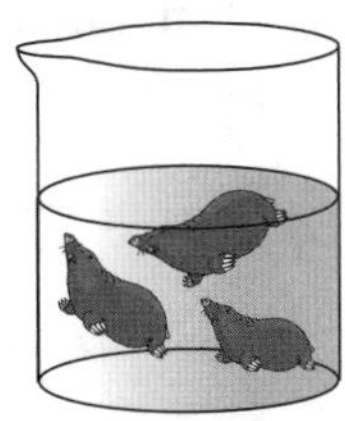

The more solute you dissolve in a given volume, the **more / less** crowded the solute molecules are and the **more / less** concentrated the solution.

b) Write down the formula for calculating the number of moles in a solution.

....

c) Use the formula to calculate the number of moles in:

i) 50 cm^3 of a 2 mol/dm^3 solution. ....

ii) 250 cm^3 of a 0.5 mol/dm^3 solution. ....

iii) 550 cm^3 of a 1.75 mol/dm^3 solution. ....

d) **200 cm^3** of a solution contains **0.25 moles** of iron hydroxide, $Fe(OH)_3$. Calculate its **molar concentration**.

....

e) What **volume** of a 1.6 mol/dm^3 solution of calcium hydroxide contains **2 moles** of calcium hydroxide?

....

Q2 Calculate the concentration of these solutions:

a) 4 moles of sodium chloride in 800 cm^3

....

b) 0.69 moles of sodium hydrogencarbonate in 300 cm^3

....

Q3 Cedric is testing substance X as a new **drug** for asthma. The drug is manufactured at a concentration of **1 mol/dm^3** and is then **diluted** before being given to patients.

He calculates that a patient taking part in the trial should take **250 ml** of a **0.2 mol/dm^3** solution of substance X each day. Describe how he could make up this strength solution.

....

....

....

....

Concentration

Q4 Calculate the volume of a **5.6 g/dm³** KOH solution that contains **0.5 moles**.

Hint: convert the concentration to mol/dm³ first.

Q5 Calculate the volume of a **223.3 g/dm³** $CuSO_4$ solution that contains **0.7 moles**.

Q6 Jared has a solution of dipotassium phosphate buffer with a concentration of **0.75 mol/dm³**.

a) Calculate how many moles are in 100 ml of this solution.

b) Jared wants to make 150 ml of 0.1 mol/dm³ dipotassium phosphate.
Describe how he could dilute the solution he has to make the new solution.

Q7 Heather needs to produce **200 cm³** of **0.1 mol/dm³** hydrochloric acid solution for an experiment. She has been provided with a **2 mol/dm³** hydrochloric acid solution and some water.

Describe how Heather could make the required solution.

Concentration

Q8 '**Froggart's**' blackcurrant cordial is **diluted** before drinking. Its contents are summarised on the label, as shown.

Froggart's blackcurrant cordial
Contains real fruit juice!
Dilute using 1 part cordial to 5 parts water.
100 ml diluted cordial contains:
8 mg vitamin C (20% GDA)
10.6 g sugar
Trace of sodium & protein
189 kJ energy

a) i) What do the letters GDA stand for?

....

ii) What does the GDA tell you?

....

b) i) Donald pours 50 ml of cordial. How much water should he add?

....

ii) What percentage of the GDA of vitamin C will this volume of cordial provide?

Work out the volume of diluted cordial first.

....

c) What volume of diluted cordial would provide 100% of the GDA of vitamin C?

....

Q9 The **nutritional information** on the label of some vegetable stock powder is shown below.

	g per 100 g stock powder	g per 250 ml serving
protein	10.5	0.5
carbohydrate	29.4	1.5
fat	8.1	0.4
fibre	0.7	0.04
sodium	17.6	0.9

a) 150 g of powder will make 7.5 litres of stock. What volume will 100 g of powder make?

....

b) Show that the mass of sodium given for a 250 ml serving agrees with that given for 100 g of powder.

....

....

c) Sodium is present mainly as sodium chloride (salt).
How much sodium chloride will 100 g of stock powder contain?

....

....

d) Suggest why this is probably an overestimate of the amount of salt in the stock powder.

....

Titrations

Q1 Describe the method for carrying out an acid/alkali titration. Include the names of any equipment that you would use.

....

....

....

....

....

Q2 An **indicator** is used to determine the **end-point** of a titration.

a) Complete the following table to show the colour of the indicators in different solutions.

Indicator	Colour in strong acid solutions	Colour in strong alkali solutions
phenolphthalein		
litmus		

b) Explain why universal indicator is **not** a suitable indicator to use in an acid-base titration.

....

....

Q3 Sophie wanted to find out the volume of an acidic solution required to neutralise 25 cm^3 of an alkaline solution. She did a rough titration first, then four more titrations. Her results are shown in the table.

Titration	Volume of acid added / cm^3
1	16.0
2	15.4
3	17.6
4	15.3
5	15.5

a) Why did Sophie carry out a rough titration at the beginning?

....

....

b) Which value is anomalous? ....

c) What is the advantage of carrying out the titration several times?

....

d) Calculate the average volume of acid needed to neutralise 25 cm^3 of the alkaline solution.

....

Titrations

Q4 The graph shows the **pH curve** from a titration.

a) Does this pH curve show an acid being added to an alkali or an alkali being added to an acid?

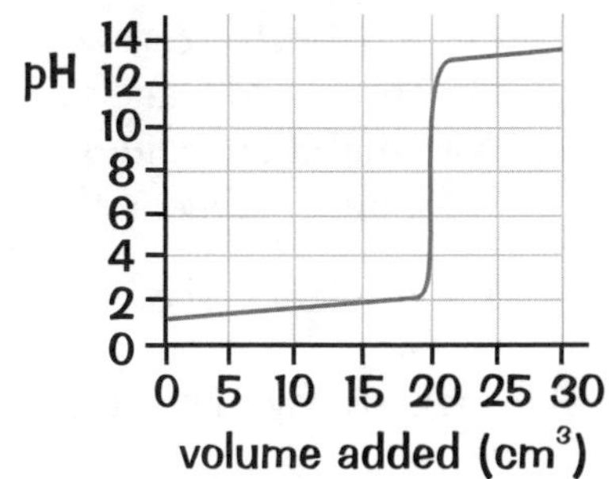

....

b) How is the end-point of a titration illustrated on a pH curve?

....

....

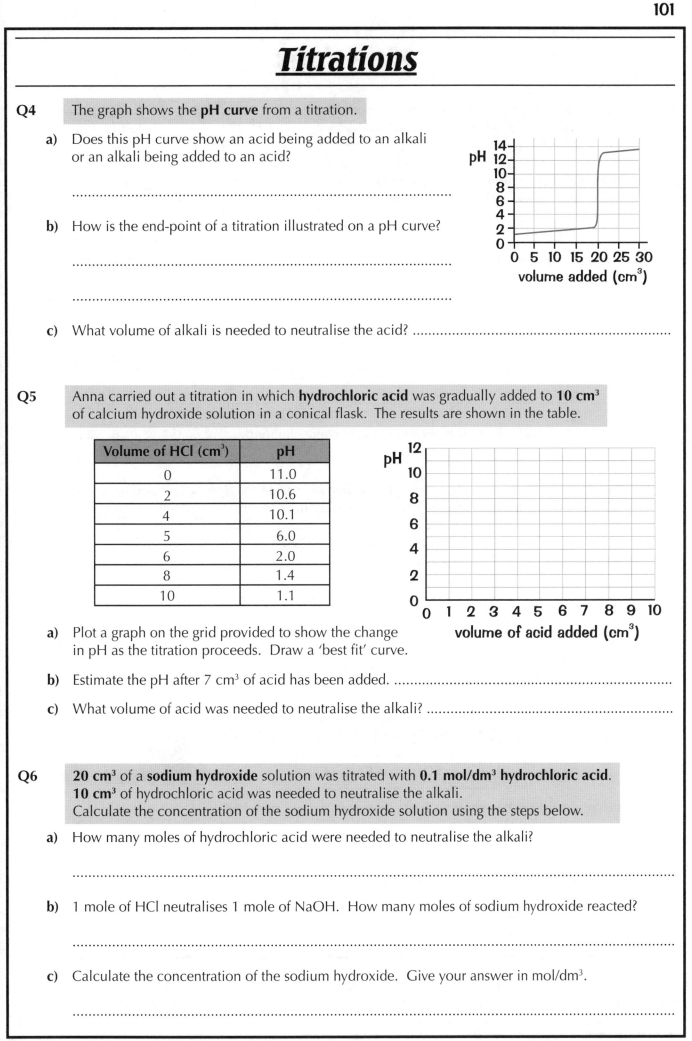

c) What volume of alkali is needed to neutralise the acid? ....

Q5 Anna carried out a titration in which **hydrochloric acid** was gradually added to **10 cm^3** of calcium hydroxide solution in a conical flask. The results are shown in the table.

Volume of HCl (cm^3)	pH
0	11.0
2	10.6
4	10.1
5	6.0
6	2.0
8	1.4
10	1.1

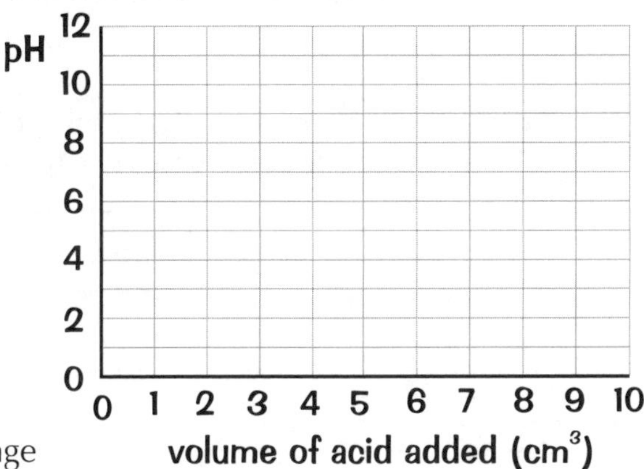

a) Plot a graph on the grid provided to show the change in pH as the titration proceeds. Draw a 'best fit' curve.

b) Estimate the pH after 7 cm^3 of acid has been added. ....

c) What volume of acid was needed to neutralise the alkali? ....

Q6 **20 cm^3** of a **sodium hydroxide** solution was titrated with **0.1 mol/dm^3 hydrochloric acid**. **10 cm^3** of hydrochloric acid was needed to neutralise the alkali. Calculate the concentration of the sodium hydroxide solution using the steps below.

a) How many moles of hydrochloric acid were needed to neutralise the alkali?

....

b) 1 mole of HCl neutralises 1 mole of NaOH. How many moles of sodium hydroxide reacted?

....

c) Calculate the concentration of the sodium hydroxide. Give your answer in mol/dm^3.

....

Titrations

Q7 Alex wanted to analyse the concentration of **phosphoric acid** in different brands of cola drinks. He allowed the carbon dioxide to escape from the drinks and titrated **20 cm³** of each drink using **0.01 mol/dm³ sodium hydroxide solution**. He used a pH meter to measure the pH.

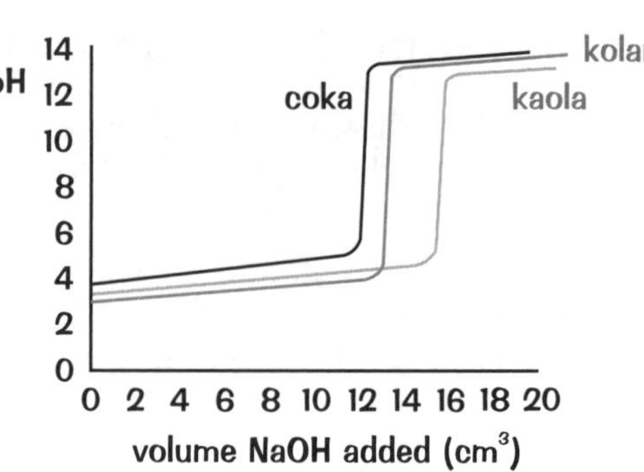

The results are shown in the graphs opposite.

a) Suggest why Alex did not use an indicator to measure pH.

....

b) Suggest why Alex allowed the carbon dioxide to escape before analysing the drinks.

.... CO_2 in water gives carbonic acid.

....

c) Which drink had the greatest phosphoric acid concentration? ....

Q8 In a titration, **12.5 cm³** of **0.04 mol/dm³ calcium hydroxide** solution was needed to neutralise **25 cm³** of **sulfuric acid**. Calculate the **concentration** of the sulfuric acid in mol/dm³.

$$H_2SO_4 + Ca(OH)_2 \rightarrow CaSO_4 + 2H_2O$$

....

....

....

Q9 In a titration, **10 cm³** of **hydrochloric acid solution** was used to neutralise **30 cm³** of **0.1 mol/dm³ potassium hydroxide solution**.

That's it! I've got the solution!

Big deal. I've got one, too.

$$HCl + KOH \rightarrow KCl + H_2O$$

What was the concentration of the hydrochloric acid in mol/dm³?

....

....

....

Top Tips: Aargh, calculations. As if Chemistry wasn't tricky enough without maths getting involved too (but at least it's not as bad as Physics). Actually, these aren't the worst calculations as long as you tackle them in stages and know your equations.

Gas Volumes

Q1 Complete the sentences by circling one answer in each pair.

a) Gas syringes can measure the **volume** / **area** of gas accurate to the nearest **dm^2** / **cm^3**.

b) A burette is **more** / **less** accurate for measuring the volume of gas collected than a measuring cylinder because the graduations on a burette are to the nearest **0.1 cm^3** / **10 cm^3**.

c) A balance can be used to measure the **volume** / **mass** of gas released in a reaction. The mass of the reactants **increases** / **decreases** as the reaction proceeds.

Q2 Choose the **most suitable method**, from A to D, for the tasks below. (Use each method once only.)

A — Bubble the gas into an upside-down gas jar filled with water.

B — Attach the conical flask to an empty boiling tube.

C — Bubble the gas into an upside-down burette filled with water.

D — Attach the conical flask to a gas syringe.

Sulfur dioxide and ammonia are soluble in water.

a) **Collecting** and **measuring** ammonia gas. ....

b) **Collecting** and **measuring** oxygen. ....

c) **Collecting** hydrogen. ....

d) **Collecting** sulfur dioxide. ....

Q3 a) What is the **volume** of **one mole** of any gas at room temperature and pressure? Circle your answer.

24 dm^3 **12 dm^3** **2.4 dm^3** **36 dm^3**

b) What volume is occupied by the following gases at room temperature and pressure?

i) 0.5 moles of hydrogen chloride. ....

ii) 6.25 moles of ammonia. ....

c) How many moles are there in the following gases at room temperature and pressure?

i) 240 cm^3 of hydrogen. ....

ii) 8 dm^3 of chlorine. ....

Following Reactions

Q1 Use the words provided to complete the passage below.

new	gas	highest	faster	reaction	reactants	slower	limiting

You can tell that a chemical .... is taking place if a .... substance is forming. You may see a colour change, a precipitate forming or a .... being given off. Reactions are .... at the start because this is when the reactants are at their .... concentrations. Eventually the reaction gets ...., and it stops when one of the .... is used up. This is called the .... reactant.

Q2 Tim adds a large piece of **magnesium** to some dilute **hydrochloric acid** and records the total volume of hydrogen gas produced every 10 seconds. His results are shown in the graph below.

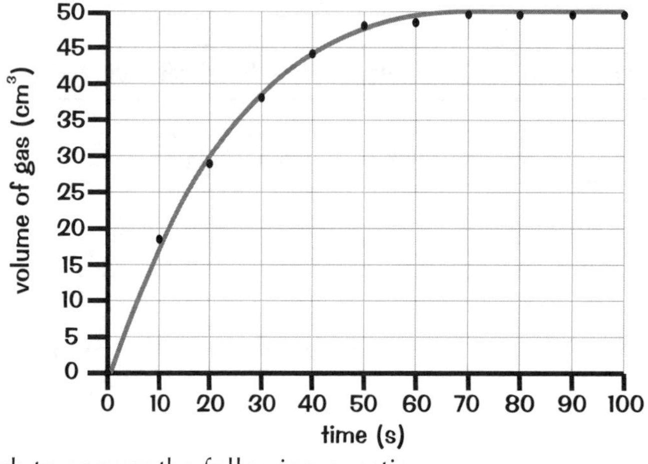

a) Use the graph to answer the following questions.

i) How long did it take for the reaction to stop? ....

ii) How much hydrogen was produced in total? ....

iii) How much gas had been formed by 25 seconds? ....

iv) How long did it take to produce 25 cm^3 of hydrogen gas? ....

b) At the end of the reaction Tim noticed that a very small piece of **magnesium** was left in the flask. Which of the reactants is the limiting reactant?

....

c) Circle the correct answer to the following questions.

i) If the amount of limiting reactant is halved, the total volume of hydrogen produced is:

25 cm^3 50 cm^3 75 cm^3 100 cm^3

ii) If the amount of limiting reactant is doubled, the total volume of hydrogen produced is:

25 cm^3 50 cm^3 100 cm^3 Not possible to predict.

Following Reactions

Q3 The graph shows the results of a reaction carried out under three different sets of **conditions**.

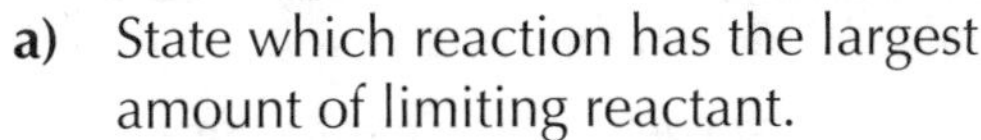

a) State which reaction has the largest amount of limiting reactant. ....

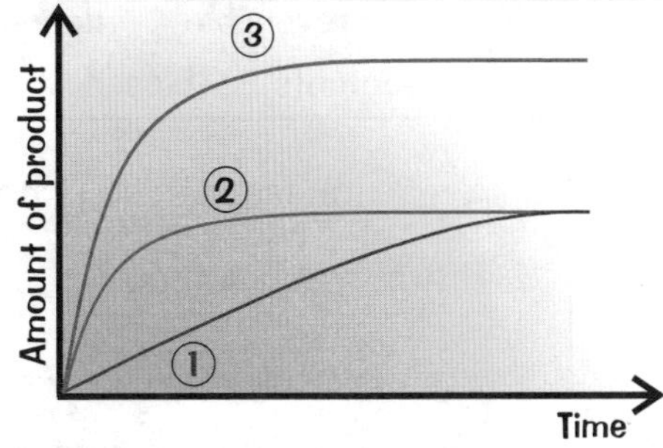

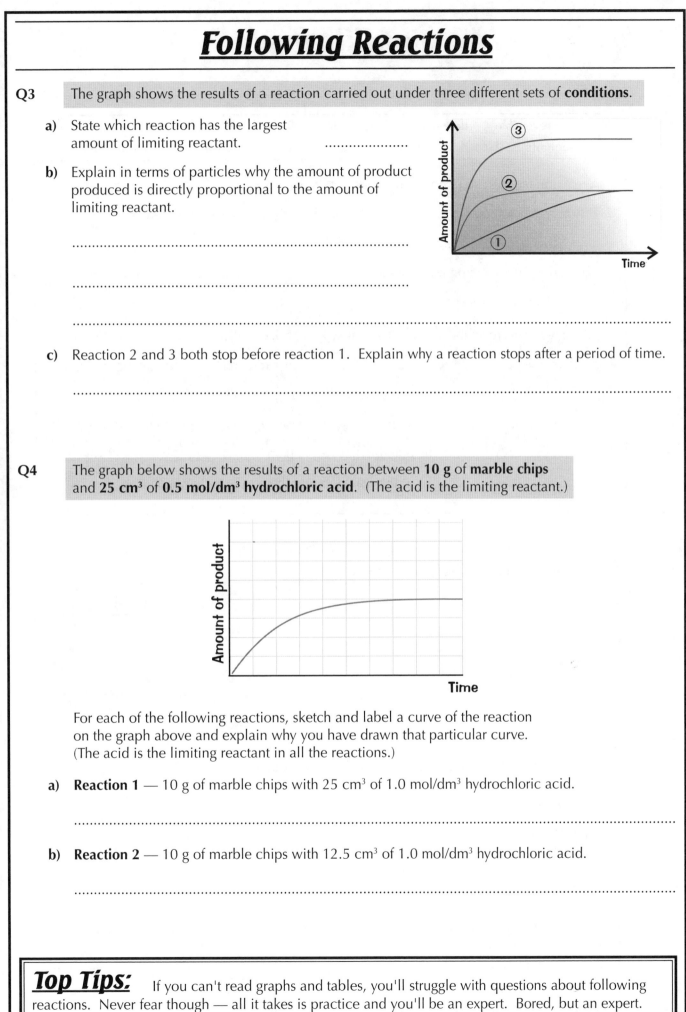

b) Explain in terms of particles why the amount of product produced is directly proportional to the amount of limiting reactant.

....

....

....

c) Reaction 2 and 3 both stop before reaction 1. Explain why a reaction stops after a period of time.

....

Q4 The graph below shows the results of a reaction between **10 g** of **marble chips** and **25 cm³** of **0.5 mol/dm³ hydrochloric acid**. (The acid is the limiting reactant.)

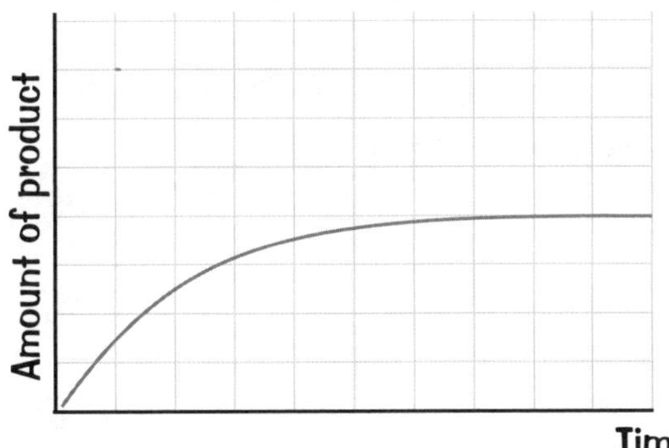

For each of the following reactions, sketch and label a curve of the reaction on the graph above and explain why you have drawn that particular curve. (The acid is the limiting reactant in all the reactions.)

a) **Reaction 1** — 10 g of marble chips with 25 cm^3 of 1.0 mol/dm^3 hydrochloric acid.

....

b) **Reaction 2** — 10 g of marble chips with 12.5 cm^3 of 1.0 mol/dm^3 hydrochloric acid.

....

Top Tips: If you can't read graphs and tables, you'll struggle with questions about following reactions. Never fear though — all it takes is practice and you'll be an expert. Bored, but an expert.

Equilibrium

Q1 Use words from the list below to complete the following passage.

reversible decrease equilibrium faster increase escape
reactants closed products react equal slower concentrations

A reaction that can go in both directions is called a .... reaction. This means that the .... of the reaction can themselves .... to give the original .... To reach equilibrium, the reaction must happen in a .... system where products and reactants can't ....

As the reactants react their concentrations will ...., so the forward reaction will get .... At the same time, the concentration of the products will ...., which makes the backward reaction get .... When the rate of the forward and backward reaction are ...., the reaction has reached an .... and the .... of the reactants and the products do not change.

Q2 Look at this diagram of a **reversible reaction**.

A
B
1
C D
A
B
2
C D

a) For the forward reaction:

i) Give the reactant(s). ....

ii) Give the product(s). ....

b) Write the equation for this reversible reaction.

....

c) Name **three** things that can change the position of an equilibrium.

....

d) State whether the concentration of the reactants will be higher, lower or the same as the concentration of the products when the position of the equilibrium is:

i) on the left. ....

ii) on the right. ....

iii) at equilibrium. ....

Changing Equilibrium

Q1 Write the letter of one equation, A to C, to which the following statements apply.

A $N_2O_4(g) \rightleftharpoons 2NO_2(g)$

B $2SO_2(g) + O_2(g) \rightleftharpoons 2SO_3(g)$

C $H_2(g) + I_2(g) \rightleftharpoons 2HI(g)$

a) A change in pressure has no effect on the position of equilibrium. ....

b) An increase in pressure moves the equilibrium to the left. ....

c) An increase in pressure moves the equilibrium to the right. ....

Q2 Substances A and B react to produce substances C and D in a reversible reaction.

$$2A(g) + B(g) \rightleftharpoons 2C(g) + D(g)$$

a) Tick the box to show which direction the equilibrium will move when the amount of one of the substances is changed.

	Left	Right
i) Amount of A increased.	☐	☐
ii) Amount of B reduced.	☐	☐
iii) Amount of C reduced.	☐	☐
iv) Amount of D increased.	☐	☐

b) The forward reaction is **exothermic**. What will happen to the amount of the reactants at equilibrium if the temperature is increased?

....

Q3 The graph shows how the percentage of **ammonia** produced during the Haber process varies with the **conditions**.

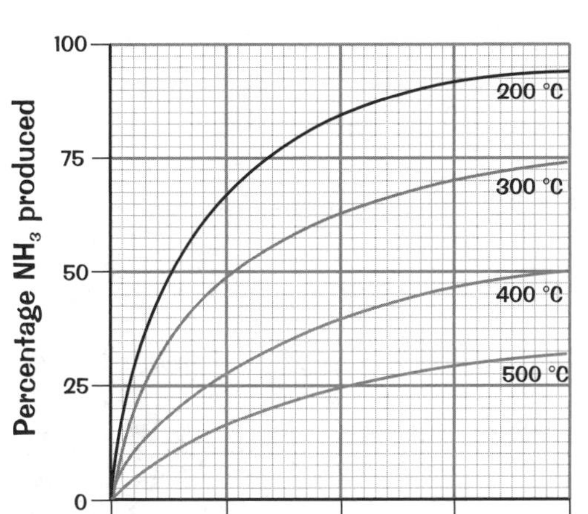

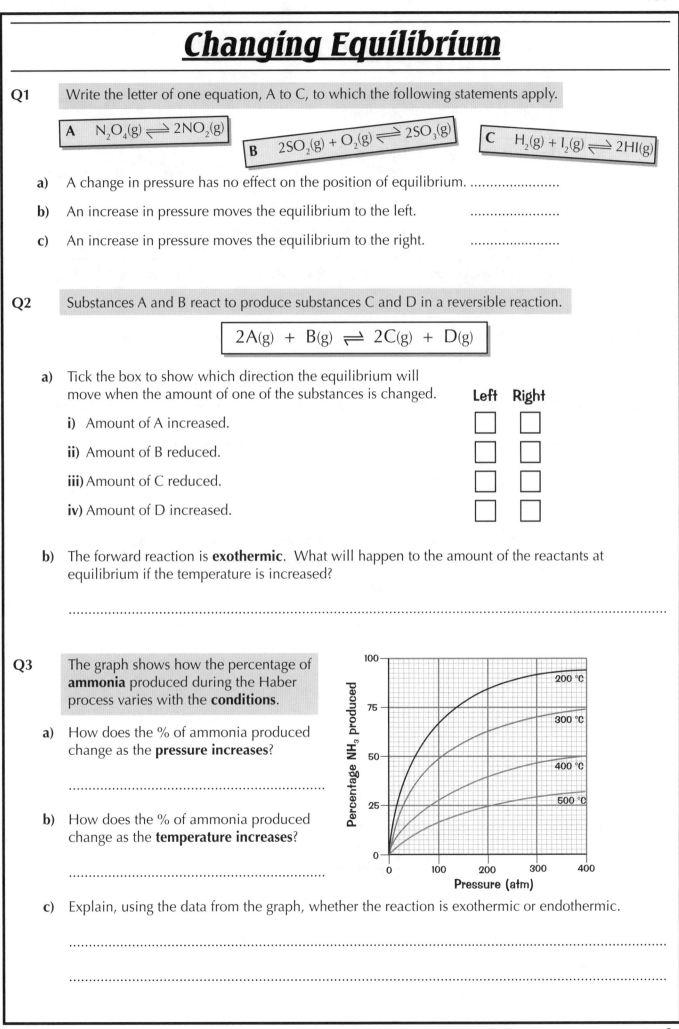

a) How does the % of ammonia produced change as the **pressure increases**?

....

b) How does the % of ammonia produced change as the **temperature increases**?

....

c) Explain, using the data from the graph, whether the reaction is exothermic or endothermic.

....

....

Changing Equilibrium

Q4 **Ethanol** is produced from **ethene** and **steam**. The equation for the reaction is given below.

$$C_2H_4(g) + H_2O(g) \rightleftharpoons C_2H_5OH(g)$$

The table shows how the percentage of ethanol at equilibrium changes as the pressure changes (at a fixed temperature).

Pressure (atm)	20	30	40	50	60	70	80	90	100
% ethanol at equilibrium	20	24	28	32	38	43	48	54	59

a) How many molecules are there on the left-hand side of the equation? ....

b) What happens to the amount of **reactants** at equilibrium when the pressure is increased?

....

c) Explain what happens to the percentage of ethanol at equilibrium when the pressure **decreases**.

....

....

Q5 For each of the following reactions, describe what would happen to the **position** of the equilibrium if the **temperature** and **pressure** of the mixture were **increased**.

a) $H_2(g) + Cl_2(g) \rightleftharpoons 2HCl(g)$ (forward reaction is exothermic)

Temperature ....

Pressure ....

b) $4NH_3(g) + 5O_2(g) \rightleftharpoons 4NO(g) + 6H_2O(g)$ (forward reaction is exothermic)

Temperature ....

Pressure ....

c) $N_2O_4(g) \rightleftharpoons 2NO_2(g)$ (forward reaction is endothermic)

Temperature ....

Pressure ....

d) $2SO_2(g) + O_2(g) \rightleftharpoons 2SO_3(g)$ (forward reaction is exothermic)

Temperature ....

Pressure ....

The Contact Process

Q1 Complete the following sentences by circling the correct word(s) in each pair.

The **reduction / oxidation** of sulfur dioxide to sulfur trioxide is **not reversible / reversible**, and the reaction is **exothermic / endothermic**.

When the temperature is increased, you get **more / less** sulfur trioxide, as the position of equilibrium is pushed to the **left / right**.

If the temperature of any reaction is increased, the rate of the reaction **decreases / increases** because the particles have **more / less** energy.

A **compromise / maximum possible** temperature of **350 °C / 450 °C** gives quite a high yield of sulfur trioxide, but produces it quite **slowly / quickly**.

Q2 **Complete** and **balance** the following equation involved in the Contact Process.

$$\ldots\ldots\ldots\ldots + \ldots\ldots\ldots\ldots \rightleftharpoons \ldots\ldots\ldots\ldots SO_3$$

Q3 The Contact Process uses **atmospheric pressure** to make sulfur trioxide.

a) Explain what happens to the yield of sulfur trioxide when the pressure is increased.

....

....

....

b) Give **two** reasons why the Contact Process is carried out at atmospheric pressure.

....

....

Q4 The Contact Process uses a catalyst.

a) State the catalyst that is used in the Contact Process.

....

b) Describe the effect of the catalyst on:

i) the rate of the reaction.

....

ii) the position of the equilibrium.

....

Strong and Weak Acids

Q1 Tick the correct boxes to show whether the following statements are **true** or **false**.

		True	False
a)	Strong acids always have higher concentrations than weak acids.	☐	☐
b)	Strong acids ionise completely in water.	☐	☐
c)	Nitric acid ionises only very slightly in water.	☐	☐
d)	Ionisation of weak acids is reversible.	☐	☐
e)	Weak acids don't form an equilibrium mixture in water.	☐	☐

Q2 Strong and weak acids react with **reactive metals** and with **carbonates** in the same way.

a) Complete the following sentences by circling the correct word(s) in each pair.

i) Hydrochloric acid and ethanoic acid react with magnesium to give **hydrogen** / **oxygen**.

ii) Hydrochloric acid and ethanoic acid react with calcium carbonate to give **carbon dioxide** / **carbon monoxide**.

b) i) Do strong acids react **faster** or **slower** than weak acids? ....

ii) Explain your answer. ....

....

....

Q3 Fill in this table by completing the equations showing the **ionisation** of these acids, with the correct **reaction symbol**, and stating whether the acid is **strong** or **weak**.

Name	Equation	Strong / Weak
Nitric acid	HNO_3 $\rightarrow$ .... + ...	....
Benzoic acid	C_6H_5COOH $\rightleftharpoons$ .... + ...	....
Hydrobromic acid	HBr .... + ...	Strong
Formic acid	HCOOH .... + ...	Weak

Top Tips: Strong and weak acids are similar but different, and it's all down to how much they ionise. If you know that weak acids only ionise a bit, all the rest pretty much follows on from there.

Strong and Weak Acids

Q4 The graph shows the results of a reaction between an excess of **magnesium** and **50 cm³ of 0.2 mol/dm³ hydrochloric acid**.

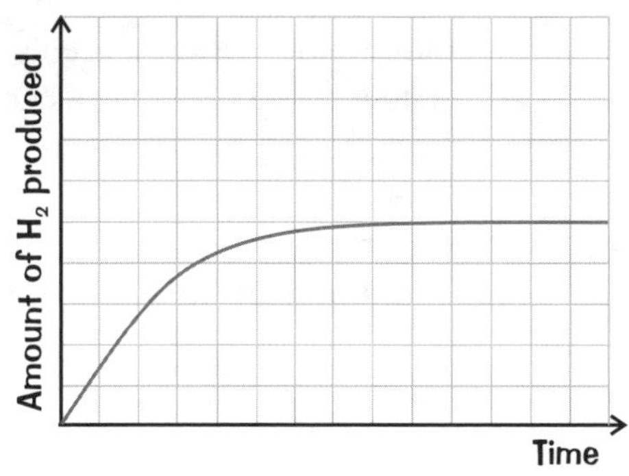

For each of the following reactions, sketch a curve on the graph above. (All of the reactions stop once the acid has run out.)

a) **Reaction 1** — Excess magnesium is reacted with 50 cm^3 of 0.4 mol/dm^3 hydrochloric acid.

b) **Reaction 2** — Excess magnesium is reacted with 50 cm^3 of 0.2 mol/dm^3 ethanoic acid.

Q5 Strong acids can be dilute and weak acids can be concentrated. Describe the difference between acid **strength** and acid **concentration**.

....

....

....

Q6 Write **equations** to show the **ionisation** of the following acids.

a) Hydrochloric acid (HCl) ....

b) Ethanoic acid (CH_3COOH) ....

Q7 Fred does an experiment to show that hydrochloric acid reacts faster than ethanoic acid with **magnesium ribbon**.

What difference would you expect to see in the amount of gas Fred collected after:

a) both acids had reacted for 20 seconds?

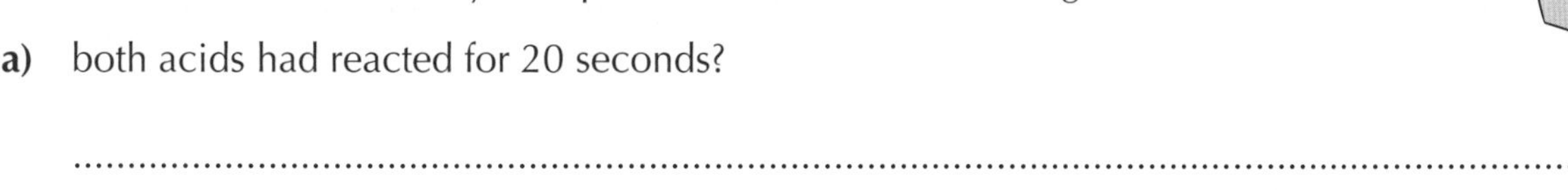

....

b) both acids had reacted completely?

....

Strong and Weak Acids

Q8 The graph below shows the volume of CO_2 released when calcium carbonate was added to flasks containing **nitric acid** or **ethanoic acid**. Both acid solutions were at the same concentration.

a) State which of the acid solutions will have a higher concentration of H^+ ions. Explain your answer.

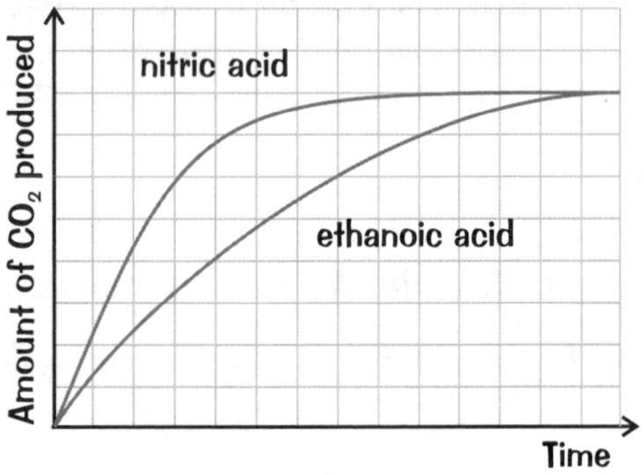

....

....

....

....

Amount of CO_2 produced

nitric acid

ethanoic acid

Time

b) Explain in terms of collision frequency why the reaction between calcium carbonate and ethanoic acid is slower than the reaction between calcium carbonate and nitric acid.

....

....

....

Q9 Explain the following:

a) The pH of nitric acid (a strong acid) is lower than the pH of lactic acid (a weak acid) (of the same concentration).

....

....

b) Hydrochloric acid is a better electrical conductor than ethanoic acid (of the same concentration).

....

....

c) Weak acids and strong acids of the same concentration will produce the same amount of product.

....

....

....

d) Electrolysis of both hydrochloric acid and ethanoic acid will produce hydrogen.

....

....

Precipitation Reactions

Q1 Look at the **equations** below, then complete the sentences by circling one answer in each pair.

barium nitrate	+	potassium sulfate	⇌	barium sulfate	+	potassium nitrate
$Ba(NO_3)_2(aq)$	+	$K_2SO_4(aq)$	⇌	$BaSO_4(s)$	+	$2KNO_3(aq)$

a) The precipitate formed is **$BaSO_4$** / **KNO_3**. This is shown by the state symbol **aq** / **s**.

b) The **potassium** / **barium** ions are spectator ions — they're **involved** / **not involved** in the reaction.

c) The ionic equation only involves the ions that **remain in solution** / **precipitate out**.

d) The reaction is **fast** / **slow** because of the **large** / **small** number of collisions.

Q2 Complete the table below to show the ionic equation and the colour of precipitate that forms when halide ions react with **Pb^{2+}** ions from lead nitrate.

Halide ion	Ionic equation	Colour of precipitate
Cl^-		
I^-		
Br^-		

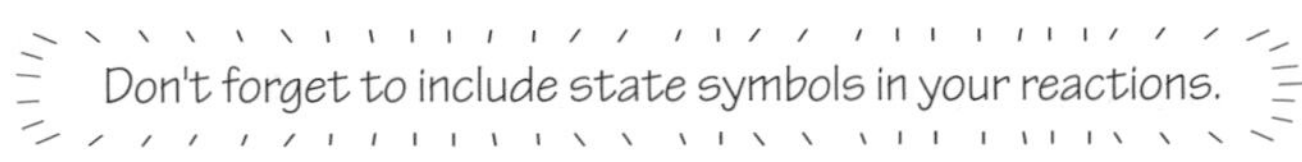

Don't forget to include state symbols in your reactions.

Q3 Jason has been given a solid sample which he suspects is **magnesium sulfate** ($MgSO_4$).

a) Describe a method Jason could use to show that the compound contains sulfate ions.

....

....

b) What is the positive result of the test described in part **a)**?

....

c) Write the word equation for this reaction.

....

Q4 Explain why **ionic substances** in precipitation reactions must be **in solution**.

....

....

Preparing Insoluble Salts

Q1 **Lead(II) nitrate** was reacted with **potassium iodide** to give an insoluble salt.

a) Which of the following is the correctly balanced symbol equation for this reaction? Tick one box.

A $PbNO_3(aq) + KI(aq) \rightarrow PbI_2(aq) + 2KNO_3(aq)$ ☐

B $Pb(NO_3)_2(aq) + 2KI(aq) \rightarrow PbI_2(s) + 2KNO_3(aq)$ ☐

C $Pb(NO_3)_2(aq) + 2KI(s) \rightarrow PbI_2(aq) + 2KNO_3(s)$ ☐

D $Pb(NO_3)_2(s) + 2KI(aq) \rightarrow PbI_2(s) + 2KNO_3(aq)$ ☐

b) Name the **insoluble salt** formed. ....

Q2 Louise wants to prepare the insoluble salt **barium sulfate**. She starts by making two solutions, one of barium nitrate and one of copper(II) sulfate.

a) Louise uses tap water to dissolve the solids.
What would be a better choice, and why?

....

b) Complete the balanced symbol equation (including state symbols) for this reaction.

$Ba(NO_3)_{2\,(aq)} + CuSO_{4\,(aq)} \rightarrow$ .... + ...

c) Describe the method used to produce the insoluble salt.

Stage 1.

....

....

Stage 2.

....

....

Stage 3.

....

....

Top Tips: The process for making an insoluble salt is always the same. So it doesn't matter what reactants they give you — the method will be the same. That makes life a lot easier.

Mixed Questions — Module C5

Q1 There are two common oxides of chromium, **oxide V** and **oxide W**.

a) 5.2 g of chromium reacted with 2.4 g of oxygen to produce oxide V.
Calculate the empirical formula of oxide V.

....

b) Oxide W has a percentage composition by mass of 52% chromium and 48% oxygen.
Work out its empirical formula.

....

Q2 During the Contact Process, **sulfur dioxide** reacts with **oxygen** to form **sulfur trioxide**.

a) Write down the balanced symbol equation for this reaction.

....

b) **i)** Is this reaction exothermic or endothermic? ....

ii) Would high or low temperatures favour a high rate of reaction? ....

c) **i)** How many moles of reactant react to produce two moles of product? ....

ii) Would high or low pressures favour a high yield of product? ....

d) **i)** What are the actual industrial conditions used during the production of sulfur trioxide?

....

ii) Why are these a compromise? ....

....

....

Q3 Simon wants to know if an unknown solution contains a **halogen**.

a) Describe a test that Simon could do to show if halide ions are present.

....

....

b) The test gives a cream precipitate.

i) Which halide ion is present? ....

ii) Write an ionic equation for the reaction. ....

Mixed Questions — Module C5

Q4 During a reaction, **0.12 g** of **magnesium** reacts completely with **20 cm³** of **nitric acid** to form **magnesium nitrate** and **hydrogen**. The acid is neutralised exactly.

$$Mg(s) + 2HNO_3(aq) \rightarrow Mg(NO_3)_2(aq) + H_2(g)$$

a) Calculate the number of moles of magnesium used.

....

b) Calculate the concentration of nitric acid used in **mol/dm³**.

....

c) i) Work out the relative formula mass of magnesium nitrate.

....

ii) Work out the mass of magnesium nitrate produced.

....

d) Calculate the volume of hydrogen gas formed (at RTP).

....

Q5 Brenda wants to find out the concentration of a solution of sodium hydroxide. She carries out a **titration** using **15 cm³** of **0.2 mol/dm³** hydrochloric acid, and finds that it takes **22 cm³** of sodium hydroxide to neutralise the acid.

a) Brenda started off with **2 mol/dm³** hydrochloric acid.
Describe how she could have made **100 cm³** of **0.2 mol/dm³** solution.

....

....

b) 1 mole of sodium hydroxide neutralises 1 mole of hydrochloric acid.
Calculate the concentration of the sodium hydroxide solution, in **mol/dm³**.

....

....

....

c) Calculate the concentration of the sodium hydroxide solution, in **g/dm³**.

....

....

Mixed Questions — Module C5

Q6 The graph opposite shows the reactions between **calcium carbonate** and two different **acids**. The reactions were carried out using identical conditions, and the same concentration and volumes of acid.

amount of gas given off (cm^3)

B

A

time (s)

a) Name the gas produced in both reactions.

....

b) Which line shows the faster reaction? ....

c) The acids are **ethanoic acid** and **hydrochloric acid**. Which line shows the reaction between **hydrochloric acid** and calcium carbonate? Explain your answer.

....

....

d) The ionisation of ethanoic acid is a **reversible reaction**. Briefly explain why changing the temperature of the ethanoic solution will cause the pH to change.

....

....

....

Remember: pH measures the number of H^+ ions in solution.

Q7 Robert wants to perform a **titration** to find the concentration of **25 cm³** of an **ethanoic acid** (CH_3COOH) solution. He wants to make **200 cm³** of a **2 mol/dm³ sodium hydroxide** (NaOH) solution to use for the titration.

a) Calculate how many **moles** of NaOH are in 200 cm^3 of a 2 mol/dm^3 solution.

....

....

b) Calculate the **mass** of NaOH needed to make the solution.

....

....

c) Robert calculates that it takes **15.7 cm³** to neutralise the ethanoic acid solution. Calculate the concentration of the ethanoic acid solution.

....

....

....

Redox Reactions

Q1 Imagine that three new metals, **antium**, **bodium** and **candium** have been discovered. The relative **reactivity** of the three metals is shown on the right.

ANTIUM
BODIUM
CANDIUM
↑ reactivity

a) A piece of pure candium is put into a solution of bodium sulfate and left for 30 minutes. Circle the correct word in the pair to complete the sentence.

After the experiment, the solution contains **candium / bodium** sulfate.

b) If a piece of pure antium is put into a solution of candium sulfate, will any antium sulfate be formed? Explain your answer.

"Ahaarr... buried antium."

....

....

Q2 Join the terms in the centre to their correct descriptions. Some terms have more than one description.

removal of oxygen
addition of oxygen
a chemical that accepts electrons and becomes reduced

oxidation
reduction
oxidising agent
reducing agent

loss of electrons
a chemical that donates electrons and becomes oxidised
gain of electrons

Q3 A piece of **magnesium** is dropped into blue **copper(II) sulfate** ($CuSO_4$) solution.

Magnesium is more reactive than copper.

a) Write a **word equation** for the reaction that takes place.

....

b) Write a **balanced** symbol equation (including state symbols) for the reaction.

....

c) Are the magnesium atoms **oxidised** or **reduced** in this reaction?

....

Q4 Zinc reacts with iron(II) sulfate solution in a **redox reaction**. Iron is produced.

a) What is a '**redox reaction**'?

....

b) During this reaction, state which metal:

i) is oxidised. .... ii) gains electrons. ....

iii) is acting as an oxidising agent. ....

Redox Reactions

Q5 **Chlorine** reacts with **iron(II) ions** to produce **chloride ions** and **iron(III) ions**. This reaction can be represented by the equation: $Cl_2 + 2Fe^{2+} \rightarrow 2Cl^- + 2Fe^{3+}$.

During this reaction, state which element:

a) loses electrons.

....

b) is reduced.

....

c) is acting as a reducing agent.

....

Please Note:
Due to printing restriction, a "Red Ox" could not be shown on this page.
Please be amused by this grey goat instead.

Q6 Graham added equal amounts of **magnesium powder** into test tubes containing **metal chloride** solutions. His observations are shown in the table on the right.

Chloride solution	Observations
iron(II) chloride ($FeCl_2$)	Solution changes colour, and gets hotter. A precipitate forms.
calcium chloride ($CaCl_2$)	Nothing happens.

a) A reaction only took place when magnesium (Mg) was added to **iron(II) chloride solution**.

i) Write a **word equation** for the reaction that takes place.

....

ii) Write a **balanced** symbol equation (including state symbols) for the reaction.

....

b) When **magnesium** was added to **iron(II) chloride solution**, which metal was:

i) oxidised? ....

ii) reduced? ....

c) Using the information in the table, state whether calcium is **more** or **less reactive** than magnesium.

....

d) Copper is **less reactive** than magnesium, calcium and iron. Predict whether a reaction would take place if Graham added powdered **iron** to a solution of **copper chloride**.

....

Top Tips: OIL RIG: **O**xidation **I**s **L**oss of electrons, **R**eduction **I**s **G**ain of electrons. An absolutely blooming **vital** thing to remember. Otherwise you risk getting all mixed up on questions like these — and you don't want that, because there are bound to be questions like these in your exam.

Rusting of Iron

Q1 Paul carries out an experiment to investigate **rusting**. He puts three **iron** nails into separate test tubes, as shown in the diagram below.

a) What **two** things are needed for iron to rust?

....

b) In which of these tubes will the iron rust most quickly?

....

c) Write a **word equation** for the formation of rust.

....

Q2 Tick the boxes to show whether each of the following statements is **true** or **false**.

	True	False
a) Painting metal items prevents them rusting by keeping out oxygen and water.	☐	☐
b) Rusting is a redox reaction.	☐	☐
c) Sacrificial protection involves a displacement reaction.	☐	☐
d) When iron rusts it loses two electrons to form Fe^{3+}.	☐	☐
e) When iron rusts the oxygen it reacts with is reduced and gains electrons.	☐	☐

Q3 Many different methods can be used to protect iron from rusting.

a) Explain why attaching magnesium bars to iron is known as 'the **sacrificial** method'.

....

b) Explain what galvanising is, and how it prevents iron from rusting.

....

....

c) Explain why coating iron with tin doesn't prevent rusting if the tin is scratched.

....

....

Q4 To prevent **iron** from rusting, it can be coated with **tin**, **paint** or **grease**. Alternatively, **magnesium bars** can be attached to the iron.

Explain which method would be most suitable for protecting **moving parts** on a very light glider.

....

....

Electrolysis

Q1 Circle the correct word(s) in each pair to complete the passage below.

During electrolysis of an ionic compound, an electric current is passed through a molten or **solid** / **dissolved** substance, causing it to **decompose** / **melt**. This **creates** / **prevents** a flow of charge through the **electrons** / **electrolyte**. Electrons are transferred to and from ions at the **electrodes** / **electrolytes**. As this happens atoms or **molecules** / **ions** are formed and **discharged** / **insulated** from the solution.

Q2 Tick the boxes to show whether these statements are **true** or **false**.

		True	False
a)	Positive ions move to the negative electrode and lose electrons.	☐	☐
b)	Negative ions move to the positive electrode and give up electrons.	☐	☐
c)	A salt will **only** conduct an electric current when molten.	☐	☐

Q3 **Sodium chloride solution** (brine) can electrolysed using the apparatus shown below.

a) Complete the labelling of the diagram.

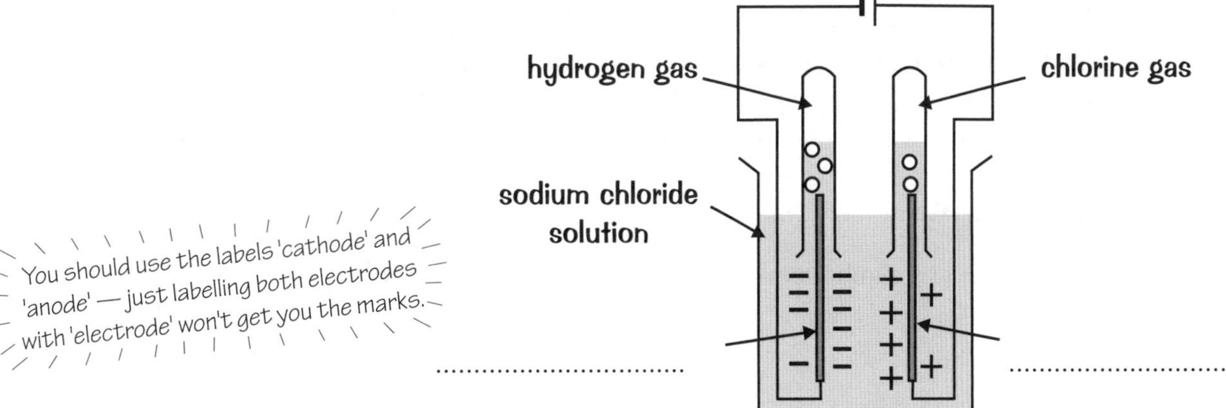

b) Complete the symbol equation for the reaction at the positive electrode:

.... $Cl^- \rightarrow Cl_2$ + ... e^-

c) Sodium chloride can also be electrolysed when molten, but not when solid. Explain why this is.

....

....

Top Tips: More vital things to remember — the cathode is negative and gives up electrons, and the anode is positive and takes up electrons. Easy to remember if, like me, you don't like cats (the **cat**hode is **negative**). If you do like cats, then sorry — you'll have to think of another way.

Electrolysis

Q4 Complete the table to show the half equations at the cathode and anode during electrolysis of the following **molten** compounds.

Ions in molten substance	Product made at cathode	Half Equation	Product made at anode	Half-Equation
Na^+, Cl^-	sodium (Na)		chlorine (Cl_2)	
Pb^{2+}, Br^-	lead (Pb)		bromine (Br_2)	
Mg^{2+}, S^{2-}	magnesium (Mg)		sulfur (S)	
Al^{3+}, O^{2-}	aluminium (Al)		oxygen (O_2)	

Q5 Roy electrolyses aqueous **sulfuric acid**, H_2SO_4.

a) Give the formulas of the **three** ions present in this solution. ....

b) **i)** Which ion is discharged at the cathode? ....

ii) Write a balanced symbol equation for the reaction at the cathode.

....

c) **i)** Which ion is discharged at the anode? Explain your answer.

....

....

ii) Write a balanced symbol equation for the reaction at the anode.

....

Q6 Andrew is electrolysing a solution of **copper(II) sulfate** ($CuSO_4$). He uses two **carbon electrodes**.

a) Name all the substances that are being formed at:

i) the positive electrode. ....

ii) the negative electrode. ....

b) Write a balanced half-equation to show the reaction at:

i) the positive electrode: ....

ii) the negative electrode: ....

Electrolysis

Q7 The table below shows the **ions** present in **aqueous solutions** of sodium hydroxide. Use this table to answer the following questions on the **electrolysis** of sodium hydroxide.

Solution	Ions present
sodium hydroxide	Na^+, H^+, OH^-

a) State the gas formed at the anode. ....

b) Write a balanced half-equation for the reaction at the anode.

....

c) Where do the H^+ ions present in the solution come from? ....

d) Hydrogen is produced at the cathode. Explain why sodium is not produced at the cathode.

....

e) Write a balanced half-equation for the reaction at the cathode.

....

f) Circle the correct word in each pair to complete the following sentences.

i) Reduction takes place at the **anode** / **cathode**.

ii) Oxidation takes place at the **anode** / **cathode**.

Q8 **Electrolysis** breaks a compound down into new substances using **electricity**.

a) Give two ways you could increase the **amount** of a substance produced during electrolysis.

1. ....

2. ....

The formula for calculating the amount of charge transferred is:

$$\mathbf{Q = I \times t}$$

where **Q** is charge in coulombs (C), **I** is current in amps (A), and **t** is time in seconds (s).

b) Calculate the charge transferred when:

i) 2.5 A has flowed for 15 s. ....

ii) 0.1 A has flowed for 30 minutes. ....

c) Calculate the time (in minutes) 6 A needs to flow for to pass 4320 coulombs.

....

Electrolysis

Q9 **Copper(II) sulfate**, $CuSO_4$, was electrolysed to produce copper at the cathode. The table below shows the results of a set of experiments to determine how much copper was produced under different conditions.

Experiment number	Current (A)	Time (minutes)	Mass of cathode before experiment (g)	Mass of cathode after experiment (g)	Mass of copper produced (g)
1	0.4	40	5.14	5.46	
2	0.6	40	5.46	5.94	
3	0.8	40	5.94	6.58	
4	1.0	40	6.58	7.30	

a) **i)** Complete the table by calculating the mass of copper produced in each experiment.

ii) Use the table to draw a graph of the results.

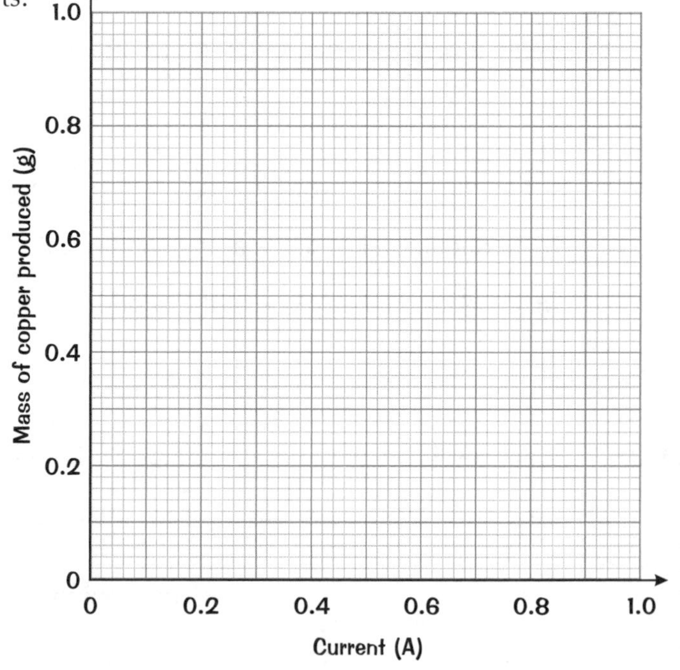

b) For one of the experiments, the current was set incorrectly.

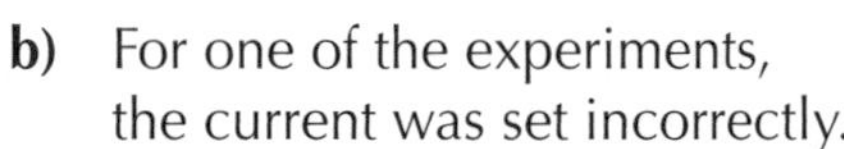

i) Suggest which experiment was incorrect.

....

ii) Use your graph to find out the actual current used in the incorrect experiment.

....

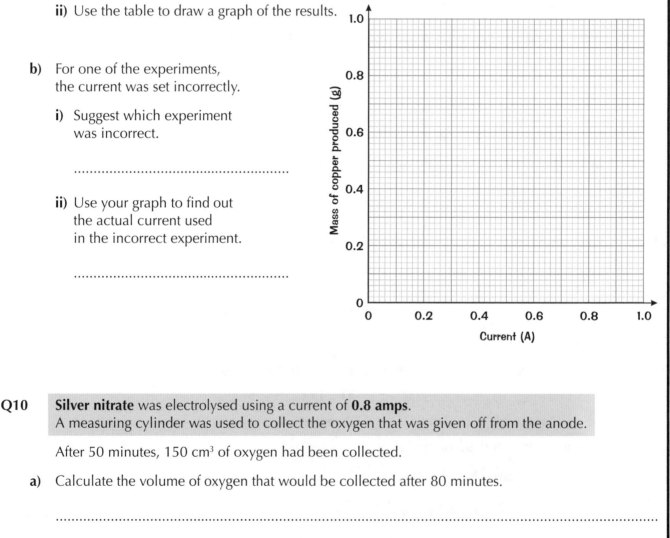

Q10 **Silver nitrate** was electrolysed using a current of **0.8 amps**. A measuring cylinder was used to collect the oxygen that was given off from the anode.

After 50 minutes, 150 cm^3 of oxygen had been collected.

a) Calculate the volume of oxygen that would be collected after 80 minutes.

....

b) How many moles of oxygen is this?

1 mole of gas = 24 dm^3

....

Fuel Cells

Q1 **Energy level diagrams** can be used to represent different types of reaction.

a) Hydrogen and oxygen react together to produce water in an exothermic reaction. Sketch an energy level diagram to show this reaction.

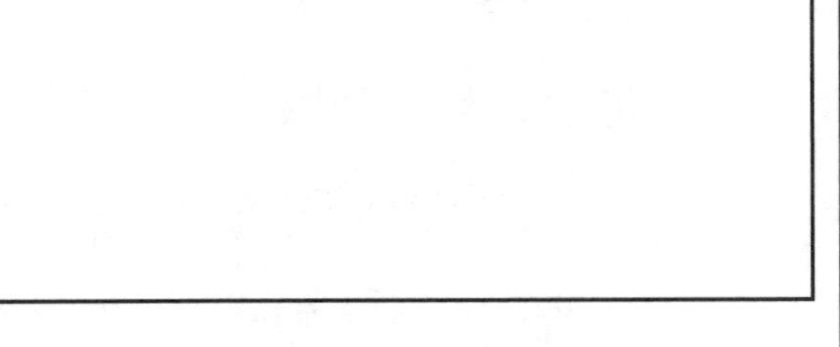

b) The energy level diagram on the right shows the energy change when oxygen reacts with nitrogen to produce nitrogen monoxide. Is this reaction endothermic or exothermic? Explain your answer.

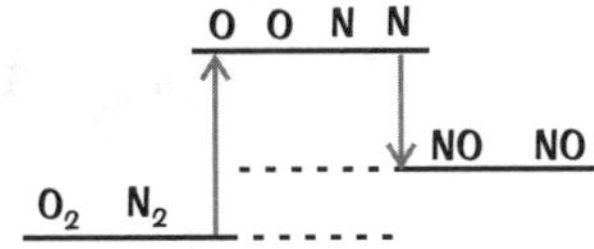

....

....

Q2 The diagram shows a hydrogen-oxygen **fuel cell**.

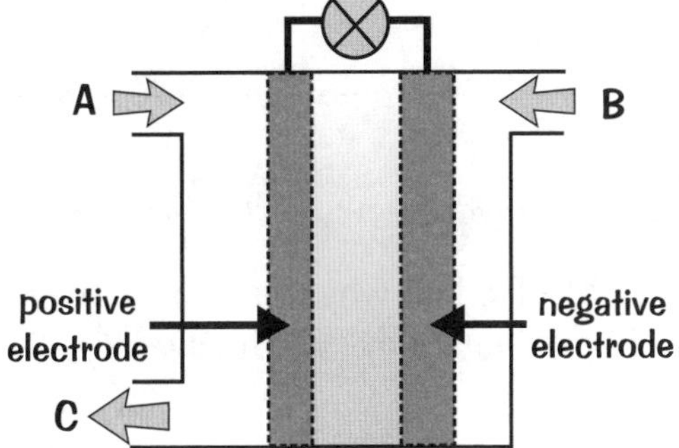

a) What goes into the cell at A and B?

A .... **B** ....

b) What comes out of the cell at C?

....

c) Complete the following sentence:

> A hydrogen-oxygen fuel cell uses energy from the .... between hydrogen and oxygen to generate .... energy efficiently.

d) Write the word equation for the overall reaction that happens in the fuel cell.

....

e) Use the ions and molecules in the box on the right to write balanced symbol equations for the reactions at the:

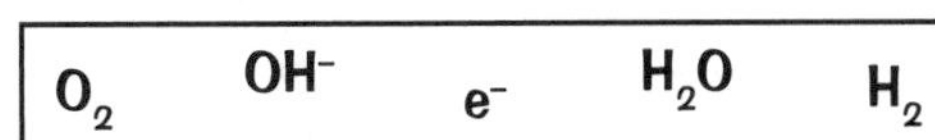

i) negative electrode. ....

ii) positive electrode. ....

f) Write a balanced symbol equation for the overall reaction that happens in the fuel cell.

....

g) Circle the correct words to complete the following sentence about the **electrodes** in a fuel cell.

Oxidation takes place at the **anode** / **cathode**, and reduction takes place at the **anode** / **cathode**.

Fuel Cells

Q3 Draw lines to connect the two halves of these sentences about **hydrogen-oxygen fuel cells**.

Fuel cells are more efficient than...

In a fuel cell electricity is generated...

Fuel cells waste less heat energy...

Fuel cells have no moving parts...

Fuel cells produce only water...

...so there is no harmful pollution.

...batteries or power stations.

...so no energy is lost due to friction.

...directly from the reaction.

...as they use fewer stages.

Q4 Give three advantages of using hydrogen fuel cells on **spacecraft**.

1. ....

2. ....

3. ....

Q5 Hydrogen fuel cells have some **environmental benefits** and some **environmental disadvantages**.

a) Explain why using cars powered by hydrogen fuel cells could lead to **less** carbon dioxide being released in cities.

....

....

b) Suggest a reason why using cars powered by hydrogen fuel cells might **not** actually **reduce** carbon dioxide emissions.

....

....

....

c) Describe **one** other possible environmental problem with hydrogen fuel cells.

....

....

d) Fossil fuels are a non-renewable energy source.
Give one reason why we will not run out of hydrogen for fuel cells.

....

....

CFCs and the Ozone Layer

Q1 **CFCs** are a **useful** group of chemicals.

a) Which of the following shows the formula of a CFC? Circle your answer.

CH_3Cl CH_3F CCl_2F_2 CH_2Cl_2

b) Which of the following are useful properties of CFCs? Circle your answer.

chemically inert | soluble in water | high boiling point

c) Give **two** uses of CFCs.

....

Q2 Say whether the following statements about **ozone** are **true** or **false**.

	True	False
a) Ozone is a form of oxygen with the formula O_3.	☐	☐
b) Most ozone is found in the lower part of the Earth's atmosphere.	☐	☐
c) Ozone does the important job of absorbing infrared light from the Sun.	☐	☐
d) When ozone absorbs the Sun's energy it breaks up into an oxygen molecule and an oxygen atom.	☐	☐

Q3 The thinning of the ozone layer is **dangerous**.

a) How does the thinning of the ozone layer affect the amount of UV radiation reaching the Earth?

....

b) Give two medical problems associated with this problem.

1. ....

2. ....

Q4 Choose from the words in the box to fill in the gaps in the passage below.

stratosphere	ions	infrared	thousands	unreactive
reactive	free radicals	one	troposphere	ultraviolet

CFCs are .... However, in the .... where there is lots of high-energy .... light, they break up to form .... Each CFC molecule produces one or more chlorine atoms which can react with .... of ozone molecules.

CFCs and the Ozone Layer

Q5 **Replacements** for CFCs are being developed.

a) Circle **two** substances from the list below that are thought to be suitable replacements for CFCs.

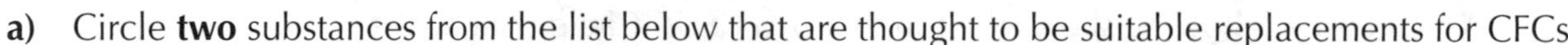

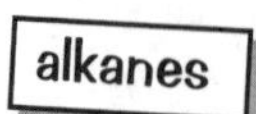

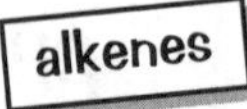

hydrofluorocarbons

b) One of the substances in the above list is a group of compounds that are very similar to CFCs. What is the important difference that makes these compounds safe to use?

....

Q6 **Free radicals** are very reactive particles.

a) Which of the dot-and-cross diagrams below correctly shows the formation of a chlorine free radical?

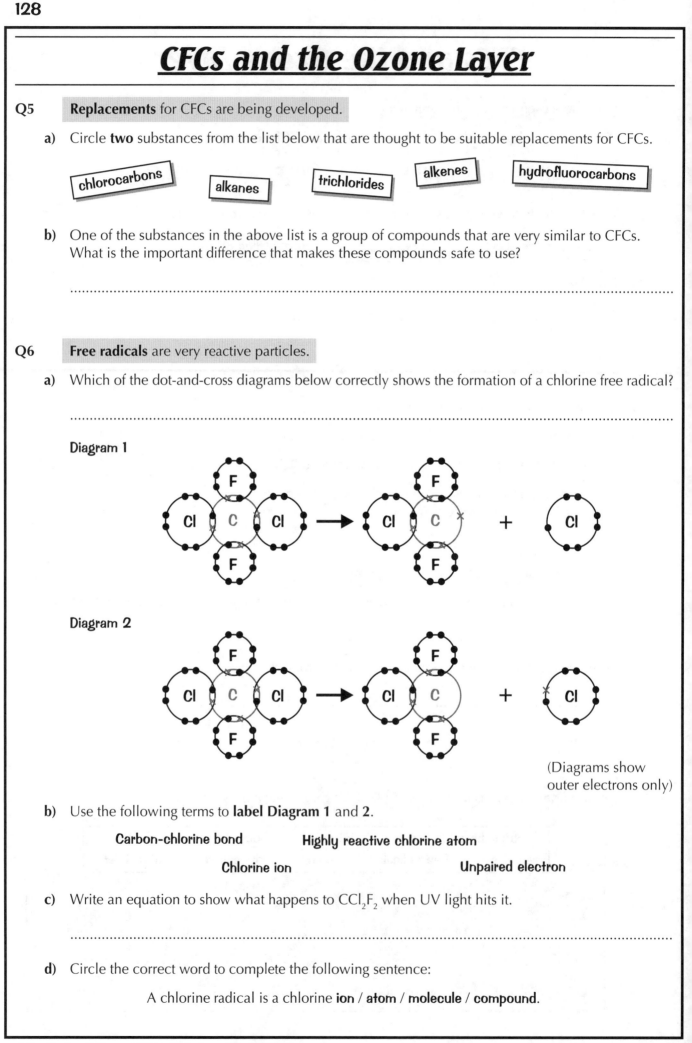

....

Diagram 1

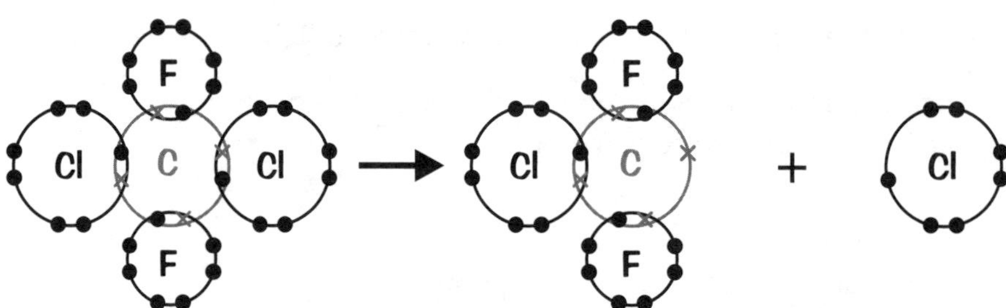

Diagram 2

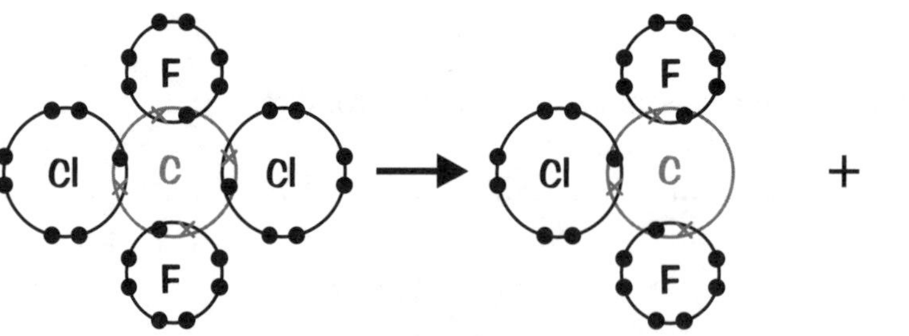

(Diagrams show outer electrons only)

b) Use the following terms to **label Diagram 1** and **2**.

Carbon-chlorine bond **Highly reactive chlorine atom**

Chlorine ion **Unpaired electron**

c) Write an equation to show what happens to CCl_2F_2 when UV light hits it.

....

d) Circle the correct word to complete the following sentence:

A chlorine radical is a chlorine **ion** / **atom** / **molecule** / **compound**.

CFCs and the Ozone Layer

Q7 CFCs damage the **ozone layer**.

a) Describe why scientists originally thought CFCs were safe to use.

....

....

....

b) Explain why even a complete ban on CFCs will not stop the damage to the ozone layer.

....

....

Q8 Circle the correct word(s) from each pair below to complete the statements about how scientists' attitudes to CFCs have **changed**.

a) In the 1970s scientists discovered that **carbon** / **chlorine** atoms can help to destroy ozone.

b) In the mid 1980s evidence was found which suggested that levels of ozone over Antarctica were **increasing** / **decreasing**.

c) Measurements in the upper atmosphere showed **high** / **low** levels of compounds produced by the breakdown of CFCs. This convinced scientists that CFCs **were** / **were not** linked to ozone depletion.

d) World leaders slowly **accepted** / **rejected** this evidence and began to ban the use of **CFCs** / **HFCs**.

Q9 **Free radicals** found in the upper atmosphere are responsible for the depletion of the ozone layer.

a) Briefly describe what's happening in the reactions below:

i) $O_3 + Cl\cdot \rightarrow ClO\cdot + O_2$

....

ii) $ClO\cdot + O_3 \rightarrow 2O_2 + Cl\cdot$

....

b) Explain why a few chlorine radicals can destroy a lot of ozone molecules.

....

....

Top Tips: CFCs were ideal for many uses — but we didn't fully understand what wider effects they'd have. Now there are loads of CFCs in the upper atmosphere, and we can't do much about it.

Hardness of Water

Q1 Tick the correct boxes to show whether the statements are **true** or **false**.

		True	False
a)	Rainwater which passes over limestone and chalk rocks becomes hard.	☐	☐
b)	Water can be softened by removing chloride and carbonate ions from the water.	☐	☐
c)	Adding sodium chloride is one way of removing hardness from water.	☐	☐
d)	Limescale is formed when soap is used with hard water.	☐	☐
e)	You can remove the hardness from water by adding sodium carbonate.	☐	☐

Q2 An **ion exchange column** can be used to remove the hardness from water.

a) Explain how hard water becomes soft when it is passed through an **ion exchange column**.

....

....

b) Does this method work for permanent hardness, temporary hardness, or both?

....

Q3 **Minerals** dissolve in water as it flows over rocks and through soil.

a) Give the **word equation** for the formation of soluble calcium hydrogencarbonate in this water.

....

b) Name the type of hardness that is caused by dissolved calcium hydrogencarbonate.

....

c) Name the type of hardness that is caused by dissolved calcium sulfate.

....

d) Washing soda is sometimes added to hard water.

i) Give the **chemical name** of washing soda.

....

ii) Describe the effect that washing soda has on hard water.

....

....

Top Tips: Hard water isn't very exciting, but at least it's not, well, hard. The only bits that will take some learning are the equations, especially that rather nasty calcium hydrogencarbonate one.

Hardness of Water

Q4 A teacher wanted to demonstrate how chalk (composed of $CaCO_3$) dissolves in rainwater to produce **hard water**, and how it forms **limescale** when it is boiled. She carried out the following experiments.

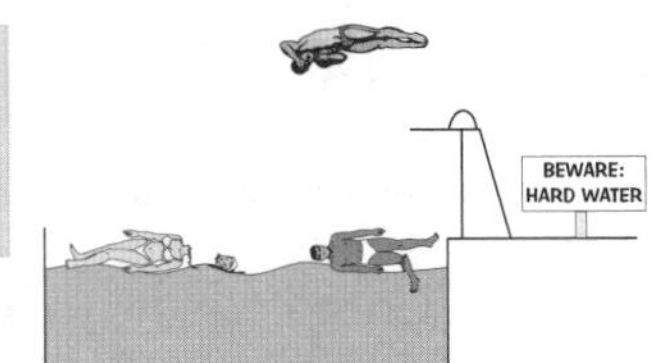

a) A spatula measure of powdered calcium carbonate was added to some distilled water and stirred. Explain why the water didn't become hard.

....

b) Carbon dioxide was bubbled through the mixture of calcium carbonate and distilled water. Explain why the water became hard.

....

....

c) A solution of calcium hydrogencarbonate was boiled in a beaker. The water became soft and a white precipitate formed.

i) Give the balanced symbol equation for this reaction. Include state symbols.

....

ii) Explain why the water became soft.

....

Q5 In an experiment to investigate the **hardness** of water from different sources, soap solution was added to samples of water. Five drops were added at a time until a good lather was formed when the samples were shaken. The experiment was then repeated with new samples of the water that had first been boiled.

Source of fresh water sample	Drops of soap solution needed to produce a lather
distilled water	5
Spondovia	35
Bogglewash	30
Oakbrook	5

Source of boiled water sample	Drops of soap solution needed to produce a lather
distilled water	5
Spondovia	35
Bogglewash	5
Oakbrook	5

a) What role did the test using distilled water play in the experiment?

....

b) **i)** Which source or sources contained **hard** water? ....

ii) Explain your answer to part **i)**.

....

c) **i)** Which source or sources contained **permanently hard** water? ....

ii) Explain your answer to part **ii)**.

....

Alcohols

Q1 **Alcohols** are a common group of chemicals.

a) Write out the general formula of an alcohol. ....

b) Complete the following table. Ethanol has been done for you.

Alcohol	No. of Carbon Atoms	Molecular Formula	Displayed Formula
Methanol	1		
Ethanol	2	C_2H_5OH	H H I I H–C–C–O–H I I H H
Propanol	3		
Butanol	4		
Pentanol	5		

Q2 The molecular formula for **ethanol** can be written as $\mathbf{C_2H_5OH}$ or as $\mathbf{C_2H_6O}$.

a) What is the functional group found in all alcohols? ....

b) Explain why it is better to write ethanol's formula as C_2H_5OH.

....

Q3 Ethanol can be made industrially by **hydrating ethene** (C_2H_4).

a) Write the **word equation** for the hydration of ethene.

....

b) Write a **balanced symbol equation** for the hydration of ethene.

....

c) Briefly describe how the reaction is carried out.

....

....

Top Tips: You may be surprised to hear that the main use of ethanol is as a **motor fuel** and **fuel additive** — not in alcoholic drinks as I previously thought. It's also used as a solvent and antiseptic.

Alcohols

Q4 Choose from the words in the box to fill in the gaps in the passage below about **fermentation**.

inactive	25 °C	35 °C	50 °C	temperature	distilled
oxygen	hot	cold	glucose solution	enzymes	ethanoic acid

Fermentation is used to turn .... into ethanol. The reaction is catalysed by .... found in yeast cells. The .... needs to be carefully controlled during the reaction — if it is too .... the yeast are .... and the reaction is very slow, but if it is too .... the yeast enzymes are denatured. The optimum is between .... and .... It is important to stop .... getting into the reaction mixture, because it converts the ethanol to .... (CH_3COOH). The reaction stops when the concentration of the ethanol gets high enough to kill the yeast cells. Then the mixture can be .... to get pure ethanol.

Q5 **Ethanol** is produced on an industrial scale to make **alcoholic drinks** and **fuel for cars**.

a) The ethanol in alcoholic drinks is produced by **fermenting glucose**.

i) Write a word equation for this reaction.

....

ii) Write a balanced symbol equation for this reaction.

....

Chateau Ethene

b) The ethanol used in car fuels can be made by **fermenting glucose** or by **hydrating ethene**.

i) Which method of producing ethanol is more **sustainable**? Explain your answer.

....

....

ii) Which method has the best **atom economy**? Explain your answer.

....

....

iii) Fermentation is a **batch** production process and ethene hydration a **continuous** production process. Briefly explain the advantages and disadvantages of each process.

....

....

....

Fats and Oils

Q1 Fats and oils come from **plants** and **animals**.

a) Name one fat or oil that comes from plants and one that comes from animals.

Plants: ....

Animals: ....

b) Give two uses of natural fats and oils.

1. ....

2. ....

Q2 Complete the passage below using some of the words in the box.

alcohols	fatty	strong	solids	acids	glycerol
esters	liquids	ethanol	gases	alkenes	

Fats are .... at room temperature and oils are ....
Fats and oils are members of a group of chemicals called ....
These chemicals can be made by reacting together .... and
.... Hydrolysis breaks up fats and oils into ....
acids and ....

Q3 Butter and milk are **emulsions** of oil and water.

a) Oil and water are **immiscible** — what does this mean?

....

b) Describe what an emulsion is, and how to make one.

....

....

c) Look at the diagrams below. Label the droplets of **oil** and the droplets of **water**.

droplets of	droplets of ....
milk	butter

Fats and Oils

Q4 Vegetable oils can be turned into **fuels**.

a) Name **one** fuel that can be made from vegetable oils.

....

b) Name a fossil fuel that your answer to part **a)** can be used as an alternative for.

....

c) A litre of "**Supreme**" biofuel contains **70%** of the energy that is found in a litre of the fossil fuel "**Megamax**". "**Megamax**" contains 37 MJ (37 000 000 J) of energy per litre. Calculate how much energy a litre of "**Supreme**" biofuel contains.

....

Q5 Oils and fats can be used to make **soap**.

a) What is **saponification**?

....

....

b) Draw lines to connect the two parts of the following sentences.

Soap is made by...	...boiling oil or fat with alkali.
The alkali usually used is...	...glycerol is produced.
As well as soap...	...sodium hydroxide.

c) Write the word equation for making soap.

....

d) Circle the correct word(s) from each pair to complete the sentences about **making soap**.

Fat molecules can be broken apart to give glycerol and fatty acids — this is an example of a **neutralisation / hydrolysis** reaction. The **glycerol / fatty acids** can then react with **sodium hydroxide / hydrochloric acid** to form soap.

Top Tips: Fats are horrible. Like when you get a nice shoulder of lamb, but you can't eat half of it because it's all fat. And then you go and learn that when you're using soap, you're kind of washing your hands with fat. Ugghh. On second thoughts, I don't think anything could beat some butter spread thickly over some freshly baked bread... ummm...

Using Plant Oils

Q1 Circle the correct word in each pair below to label each fatty acid structure.

a) **Saturated / unsaturated** grape seed oil

b) **Saturated / unsaturated** olive oil

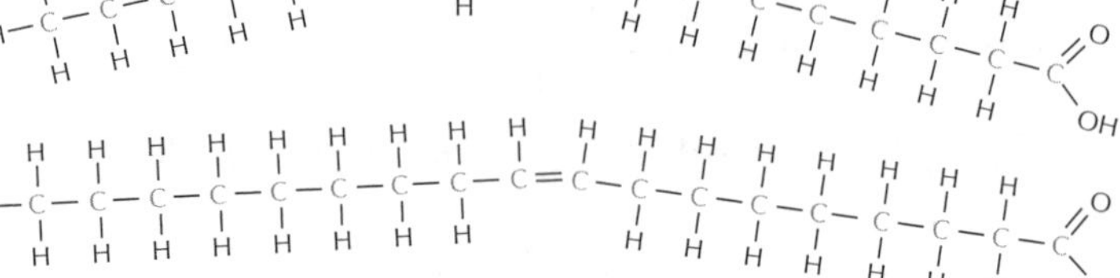

c) **Saturated / unsaturated** animal fat

Q2 Ben has two test tubes. One contains a sample of an **unsaturated fat** and the other has a sample of a **saturated fat**. He adds some **bromine water** to both tubes and shakes them.

a) After Ben added the bromine water, the substance in the **first test tube** stayed orange. State whether the substance in the **first tube** is a sample of saturated fat or unsaturated fat.

b) i) Describe what you would see happening in the **second test tube** as Ben shakes it.

ii) Briefly describe the reaction that is taking place in the **second test tube**.

Q3 Margarine is usually made from **partially hydrogenated** vegetable oil.

a) Describe how hydrogenation is carried out.

b) Describe how hydrogenation affects the chemical structure of vegetable oils.

Q4 State which are less healthy, **saturated** or **unsaturated** fats. Explain your answer.

Detergents

Q1 Tick the boxes to show whether these statements about **dry cleaning** are **true** or **false**.

True False

a) **Dry cleaning** means any cleaning process that involves using **water** as a **solvent**. ☐ ☐

b) **Dry cleaning** can be used to remove **stains** that will not **dissolve** in **water**. ☐ ☐

c) There are **strong intermolecular forces** between the molecules in a **grease** stain. ☐ ☐

d) Molecules **of dry cleaning solvents** have **weak intermolecular forces** between them. ☐ ☐

e) As you add the solvent, **intermolecular forces** form between the solvent molecules and the grease molecules. ☐ ☐

f) When the **solvent** is removed the **grease molecules** are left behind. ☐ ☐

Q2 The diagram shows a **detergent molecule**.

a) Complete the diagram by labelling the **hydrophilic** and **hydrophobic** sections of the molecule.

....

b) Explain how the structure of a detergent molecule helps it to remove oily stains in the wash.

....

....

....

Q3 Felicity works for a chemical company that is developing a new **washing powder**. She tests five different powders and records their **cleaning effectiveness** at different temperatures against a range of stains. She uses a scale of **1** (**poor**) to **10** (**excellent**).

a) Felicity's results are shown in the table on the right.

i) State which powder is best at cleaning grass stains at 30 °C.

....

ii) Which powders contain **enzymes**? Explain your answer.

....

....

....

		Washing powder				
		A	B	C	D	E
Effectiveness	Stain: tomato Temperature: 30 °C	8	3	5	8	8
	Stain: tomato Temperature: 50 °C	3	3	9	8	3
	Stain: grass Temperature: 30 °C	7	4	5	8	9
	Stain: grass Temperature: 50 °C	3	4	8	9	3

b) Some of the washing powders work best at lower temperatures.
Give two advantages of being able to wash your clothes at lower temperatures.

1. ....

2. ....

Mixed Questions — Module C6

Q1 Sam is using **electrolysis** to split **lead(II) iodide** (PbI_2) into **pure solid lead** and **iodine gas**.

a) Sam has to melt the lead(II) iodide before he can electrolyse it.
Explain why he cannot electrolyse **solid** lead(II) iodide.

....

....

b) Sam's molten lead(II) iodide contains **lead ions** (**Pb^{2+}**) and **iodide ions** (**I^-**).

i) State whether the solid lead is formed at the **anode** or at the **cathode**. ....

ii) Write the half-equation for the reaction that takes place at the **anode**.

....

c) Lead is **more reactive** than copper. Describe what will happen to the metals if Sam adds some of his pure lead to a solution of copper chloride.

....

....

Q2 **Hydrogen-oxygen fuel cells** involve a **redox reaction**.

a) Draw a line to join each electrode to the correct half-equation for the reaction that takes place there.

$O_2 + 2H_2 \rightarrow 2H_2O$

Cathode

$O_2 + 4e^- + 2H_2O \rightarrow 4OH^-$

$2H_2 + 4OH^- \rightarrow 4H_2O + 4e^-$

Anode

$2H_2O \rightarrow O_2 + 2H_2$

b) Explain why the reaction is classed as a **redox reaction**.

....

....

c) Give one **advantage** of using hydrogen fuel cells instead of petrol to power a car engine.

....

Q3 The Forth Rail Bridge is the second longest cantilever bridge in the world. It is made of over 50 000 tonnes of **steel**, it is 2.5 km long and it is **painted** all over.

a) Give one reason why it is necessary to paint the bridge.

....

b) Another type of steel is used for making cutlery, but this doesn't need to be painted. Explain why.

....

....

Mixed Questions — Module C6

Q4 The diagram opposite shows the electrolysis of **copper(II) sulfate solution**, with copper electrodes.

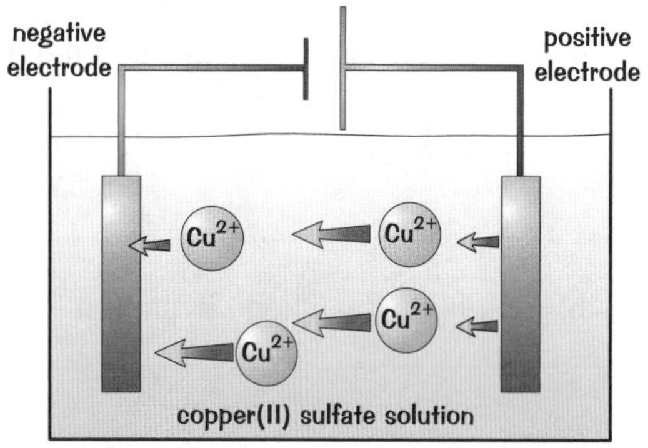

negative electrode
positive electrode
Cu^{2+}
Cu^{2+}
Cu^{2+}
Cu^{2+}
copper(II) sulfate solution

a) Complete the half-equations for the reaction at each electrode.

i) At the positive electrode:

Cu → .... + ...

ii) At the negative electrode:

Cu^{2+} + ... → ....

b) **i)** If 5 g of copper formed at the negative electrode, state the mass of copper that was lost from the positive electrode.

....

ii) If 2 amps flows through the solution of copper(II) sulfate for 30 minutes, 1.2 g of copper is formed at the negative electrode. Calculate how long it would take for **5 g** of copper to form if a current of **5 amps** flows through the solution.

....

....

....

....

Q5 **Chlorine free radicals** act on ozone in the stratosphere.

a) Briefly describe how chlorine free radicals are produced from CFCs.

....

b) One chlorine free radical can break up a large number of ozone molecules. Why is this?

....

....

c) Since the 1990s, butane has been used as a propellant in aerosols in Europe.

i) Explain why alkanes are a better alternative to CFCs.

....

ii) Suggest another safe alternative to CFCs.

....

Mixed Questions — Module C6

Q6 **Ethanol** can be produced by **fermentation** or by the **hydration** of **ethene.**

a) Describe **one** advantage that the hydration of ethene has over fermentation.

....

....

b) Explain why ethene hydration is a more expensive method of producing ethanol than fermentation.

....

....

Q7 Hyde tested samples of water from three different **rivers** using the following method.

1. 8 cm^3 of river water was placed in a test tube.
2. 1 cm^3 of soap solution was added and the tube was shaken.
3. More soap was added until a lasting lather was produced.
4. The amount of soap solution needed was recorded.
5. The experiment was repeated with boiled water from the river.

shake
shake
shake

The results of the experiment are shown in the table.

RIVER	AMOUNT OF SOAP NEEDED (cm^3)	
	PLAIN WATER	BOILED WATER
A	7	5
B	2	2
C	4	4

a) Which river contained the softest water? ....

b) Which river contained the hardest water? ....

c) Why was less soap needed to form a lasting lather after the water from river A was boiled?

....

....

Q8 Paul has two samples of **vegetable oil**, one is saturated, one is unsaturated.

a) Describe a chemical test that Paul could use to tell which oil is saturated.

....

....

b) Which of the oils is likely to be better for your **health** if used in cooking? Explain your answer.

....

....

c) Apart from cooking, name **one** other use for vegetable oils.

....